Skills Link™

Everyday
Mathematics®

Skills Link™

Everyday Mathematics®

Cumulative Practice Sets

A Division of The McGraw-Hill Companies

Columbus, Ohio
Chicago, Illinois

Photo Credits

Cover: Bill Burlingham/Photography

Photo Collage: Herman Adler Design

www.sra4kids.com

SRA/McGraw-Hill

*A Division of The **McGraw·Hill** Companies*

Send all inquiries to:
SRA/McGraw-Hill
P.O. Box 812960
Chicago, IL 60681

Printed in the United States of America.

ISBN 1-57039-968-9

4 5 6 7 8 9 VHG 07 06 05 04 03 02

Contents

Practice Set 1

Write all of your answers on a separate sheet of paper.

Write the letter of the array that matches the number model.

1. 2 * 5 = 10

2. 4 * 3 = 12

3. 1 * 8 = 8

4. 3 * 4 = 12

5. 2 * 4 = 8

A. ● ● ● ● ● ● ● ● ●

B. ● ● ● ●
   ● ● ● ●

C. ● ● ● ●
   ● ● ● ●
   ● ● ● ●

D. ● ● ● ● ●
   ● ● ● ● ●

E. ● ● ●
   ● ● ●
   ● ● ●
   ● ● ●

Round to the nearest hundred.

6. 699   **7.** 2,208   **8.** 7,942

9. 51,985   **10.** 22,761   **11.** 17,032

Complete the following number lines.

12.

0 ■ 0.4 ■ ■   1

13.

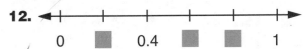

15 ■ 25   30 ■

14.

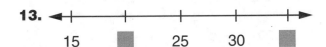

4 ■ ■   16 ■ 24

15.

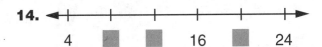

■ ■ ■ $\frac{3}{5}$ ■ 1

Practice Set 2

Write all of your answers on a separate sheet of paper.

In each set of problems below, do as many exercises as you can in one minute.

Problem Set 1	Problem Set 2	Problem Set 3
1. 5 * 2 10	**16.** 9 * 4 36	**31.** 2 * 11 22
2. 6 * 10 60	**17.** 7 * 8 56	**32.** 3 * 10 30
3. 2 * 4 8	**18.** 8 * 3 24	**33.** 1 * 4 4
4. 3 * 5 35	**19.** 9 * 2 18	**34.** 4 * 3 12
5. 8 * 6 48	**20.** 9 * 6 54	**35.** 3 * 7 21
6. 8 * 7 56	**21.** 5 * 10 50	**36.** 5 * 3 15
7. 11 * 5 55	**22.** 5 * 6 30	**37.** 11 * 0 0
8. 7 * 6 42	**23.** 4 * 8 32	**38.** 9 * 5 45
9. 5 * 4 20	**24.** 6 * 3 18	**39.** 5 * 8 40
10. 6 * 7 42	**25.** 3 * 8 24	**40.** 6 * 2 12
11. 7 * 9 63	**26.** 10 * 10 100	**41.** 4 * 4 16
12. 7 * 4 28	**27.** 9 * 5 45	**42.** 7 * 7 49
13. 6 * 9 54	**28.** 7 * 3 21	**43.** 9 * 11 99
14. 8 * 2 16	**29.** 3 * 11 33	**44.** 3 * 12 36
15. 2 * 10 20	**30.** 0 * 9 0	**45.** 4 * 4 16

2

SRB
192
204 227

Write all of your answers on a separate sheet of paper.

Table of Equivalents	
3 * 4 3 × 4	12 / 3 12 ÷ 3 $\frac{12}{3}$ $3\overline{)12}$

Solve.

46. 250
× 4

47. 525
− 78

48. 184
− 67

49. 21
+ 55

50. 35
+ 24

51. 39
+ 16

52. 19
× 30

53. 531
+ 721

54. 1,800
− 744

55. (60 + 30) * 5

56. 38 − (6 * 6)

57. 48 + 22 + 27

58. (63 / 9) * 7

Round to the nearest thousand.

59. 47,983

60. 5,255

61. 76,529

62. 383,051

Write the coordinates of the points shown on the coordinate grid.

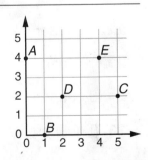

63. A 0,4

64. B 1,0

65. C 5,2

66. D 2,2

67. E 4,4

Write all of your answers on a separate sheet of paper.

Write the numbers from 30 to 50. Use those numbers to answer Items 1–4.

1. List the even numbers.

2. List the odd numbers.

3. List the numbers that have 5 as a factor.

4. List the numbers that have 4 as a factor.

Solve.

5. 5 + 4 _9_   **6.** 12 − 4 _8_   **7.** 10 + 7 _17_

8. 11 − 5 _55_   **9.** 9 + 6 _15_   **10.** 11 − 8 _3_

11. 6 + 8 _14_   **12.** 13 − 9 _4_   **13.** 12 − 5 _7_

14. 17 − 8 _9_   **15.** 8 + 8 _16_   **16.** 15 − 6 _9_

17. 3 + 7 _10_   **18.** 9 − 9 _0_   **19.** 7 + 9 _16_

Write each of the following in dollars-and-cents notation.

20. 4 quarters, 3 dimes, 2 nickels, 4 pennies

21. 6 quarters, 6 dimes, 1 nickel, 2 pennies

22. 5 quarters, 2 nickels

23. 10 quarters, 18 nickels

24. 8 quarters, 5 nickels, 7 dimes

25. 9 quarters, 10 dimes, 5 pennies

Write all of your answers on a separate sheet of paper.

Use divisibility tests to help you answer these questions. Write *yes* or *no*.

1. Is 300 divisible by 5?

2. Is 752 divisible by 2?

3. Is 5,225 divisible by 3?

4. Is 39,105 divisible by 9?

5. Is 18,373 divisible by 5?

6. Is 103,748 divisible by 10?

Write the numbers in order from least to greatest.

7. $\frac{7}{10}, \frac{5}{10}, \frac{9}{10}, \frac{3}{10}, \frac{6}{10}$

8. $\frac{3}{5}, \frac{3}{7}, \frac{3}{4}, \frac{3}{2}, \frac{3}{8}$

9. $\frac{1}{2}, \frac{3}{5}, \frac{1}{4}, \frac{7}{10}, \frac{11}{12}$

Make name-collection boxes for the numbers below. Use as many different numbers and operations as you can.

Example

189
$(60 * 3) + 9$
$378 / 2$
$(200 - 15) + 4$

10. 138

11. 79

12. 402

Write all of your answers on a separate sheet of paper.

Complete.

13. $10^3 = \blacksquare$ **14.** $10^\blacksquare = 10,000$

15. $10 * 10 * 10 * 10 * 10 = \blacksquare$

16. 10 to the eighth power $= \blacksquare$

Rewrite the number models with parentheses to make them correct.

17. $7 * (9 - 4) = 35$ **18.** $(7 * 9) - 4 = 59$

19. $(32 - 16) - 7 = 9$ **20.** $32 - (16 - 7) = 23$

21. $(4 * 9) + (3 * 12) = 72$ **22.** $40 = (5 * 7) + 5$

23. $60 = 5 * (7 + 5)$ **24.** $589 = 6 * (25 + 75) - 11$

Solve.

25. How many 8s in 2,400?   **26.** How many 7s in 7,700?

27. $\begin{array}{r} 2,000 \\ + 43 \\ \hline \end{array}$ **28.** $\begin{array}{r} 150 \\ * 30 \\ \hline \end{array}$ **29.** $\begin{array}{r} 2,500 \\ * 5 \\ \hline \end{array}$ **30.** $\begin{array}{r} 175 \\ * 20 \\ \hline \end{array}$

31. $\begin{array}{r} 428 \\ * 8 \\ \hline \end{array}$ **32.** $\begin{array}{r} 92 \\ * 15 \\ \hline \end{array}$ **33.** $\begin{array}{r} 800 \\ * 45 \\ \hline \end{array}$ **34.** $\begin{array}{r} 750 \\ * 18 \\ \hline \end{array}$

35. $6)\overline{78}$ **36.** $30)\overline{4,500}$ **37.** 450 / 9

38. A soup company offered to donate 40¢ for every soup-can label a school turned in. Forty-three students at Audubon School each brought in 25 soup can labels. How many soup-can labels did all the students bring in?

39. How much would the soup company donate to Audubon School?

Use with or after Lesson 1.5.

Write all of your answers on a separate sheet of paper.

Write *prime* or *composite* for each number.

1. 18   **2.** 17   **3.** 39

4. 43   **5.** 50   **6.** 23

7. 42   **8.** 77   **9.** 37

Find the area of each rectangle and write the number model.

| Area = length (*l*) × width (*w*) |

Example   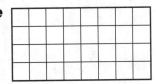   4 ∗ 8 = 32 square units

10.   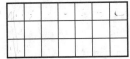   21 units²

11.   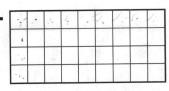   36 units²

Write all of your answers on a separate sheet of paper.

Write each decimal as a percent.

12. 0.40   **13.** 0.25   **14.** 0.12

15. 0.85   **16.** 1.67   **17.** 0.05

Complete the number lines.

18.

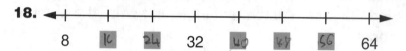

8   16   24   32   40   48   56   64

19.

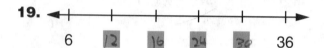

6   12   16   24   30   36

20.

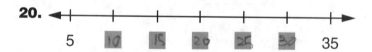

5   10   15   20   25   32   35

21.

9   29   39   69   89

22.

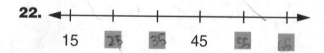

15   25   35   45   55   6

23.

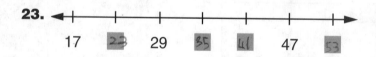

17   23   29   35   41   47   53

24.

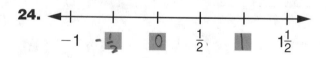

-1   -½   0   ½   1   1½

Write all of your answers on a separate sheet of paper.

Write the letter of the square array that matches the square number.

1. 36

A.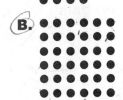

2. 64

B.

3. 16

C.

4. 9

D.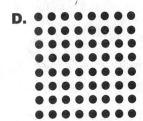

List all the factors of each number. Tell whether each number is *prime* or *composite*.

5. 24   **6.** 50   **7.** 17   **8.** 44

Compare. Write < or >.

9. 33,085 ■ 13,058   **10.** 41,123 ■ 13,058

11. 110,362 ■ 101,317   **12.** 583,627 ■ 588,267

Write the digit in the thousands place.

13. 71,345   **14.** 836,210   **15.** 9,219

16. 415,740   **17.** 307,912   **18.** 1,927,435

Write all of your answers on a separate sheet of paper.

Write each of the following in standard notation.

19. 4^2 **20.** 12^2 **21.** 27^2

22. 25^2 **23.** 40^2 **24.** 62^2

Six people are going to share $111 equally.

25. How many $100 bills does each person get?

26. How many dollars are left to share?

27. How many $10 bills does each person get?

28. How many dollars are left to share?

29. How many $1 bills does each person get?

30. How many dollars are left over?

31. If the leftover money is shared equally, how many cents does each person get?

32. Write a number model for the above problem.

Solve.

33. $210 - 180$ **34.** $526 + 127$

35. $80 + 36$ **36.** $52 - 17$

37. $97 - 8$ **38.** $90 * 9$

39. $587 - 236$ **40.** $2,662 - 141$

41. $370 * 8$ **42.** $262 + 3,455$

43. $120 * 50$ **44.** $2,625 + 5,213$

Write all of your answers on a separate sheet of paper.

Write the letter that matches the square root for each number.

1. 49
2. 0.25
3. 169
4. 400

A. 0.5
B. 13
C. 20
D. 7

Tell whether each number is a square number. Write *yes* or *no*.

5. 64   6. 177   7. 90

8. 144   9. 225   10. 250

Write the number sentences with parentheses and solve.

11. Add 70 to the difference of 365 and 36.

12. Subtract the sum of 24 and 13 from 48.

13. Add 7 to the difference of 37 and 15.

14. Subtract the sum of 18 and 222 from 428.

Write the following numbers in digits.

15. eighty million, three hundred twenty-one thousand, nine hundred eleven

16. two billion, fifty-six thousand, five hundred

17. six hundred fourteen billion, three hundred million

Practice Set 8

SRB
6 12
123

Write all of your answers on a separate sheet of paper.

Rewrite each product using exponents.

1. $3 * 3 * 3$

2. $3 * 3 * 5 * 5 * 5$

3. $2 * 2 * 7 * 7$

4. $5 * 5 * 7 * 7$

5. $3 * 3 * 11 * 11$

6. $5 * 5 * 5 * 5$

Tell which is the prime factorization for each number.

7. 16 $2 * 2 * 2 * 2$ or $2 * 2 * 2 * 4$

8. 9 $2 * 3$ or $3 * 3$

9. 30 $3 * 10$ or $2 * 3 * 5$

Use the spinner for items 10–12. Supppose you spin a paper clip on the base of the spinner. Write *true* or *false* for each statement.

10. The paper clip is most likely to land on black.

11. The paper clip is least likely to land on red.

12. The paper clip is equally likely to land on black as on white.

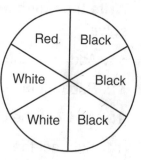

Solve.

13. $\begin{array}{r} 20 \\ + 17 \\ \hline \end{array}$

14. $\begin{array}{r} 31 \\ - 15 \\ \hline \end{array}$

15. $\begin{array}{r} 38 \\ + 24 \\ \hline \end{array}$

16. $\begin{array}{r} 320 \\ - 160 \\ \hline \end{array}$

17. $\begin{array}{r} 560 \\ + 481 \\ \hline \end{array}$

18. $\begin{array}{r} 745 \\ - 260 \\ \hline \end{array}$

Use with or after Lesson 1.9.

Practice Set 8 (cont.)

Write all of your answers on a separate sheet of paper.

In each set of problems below, do as many exercises as you can in one minute.

Problem Set 1	Problem Set 2	Problem Set 3
19. 108 / 9	**34.** 9 * 6	**49.** 6 * 6
20. 44 / 4	**35.** 7 * 7	**50.** 12 * 11
21. 121 / 11	**36.** 12 * 8	**51.** 8 * 4
22. 90 / 9	**37.** 2 * 10	**52.** 3 * 8
23. 132 / 12	**38.** 11 * 4	**53.** 4 * 10
24. 12 * 5	**39.** 12 * 6	**54.** 64 / 8
25. 10 * 11	**40.** 3 * 11	**55.** 49 / 7
26. 12 * 7	**41.** 12 * 9	**56.** 144 / 12
27. 9 * 7	**42.** 4 * 7	**57.** 21 / 3
28. 4 * 12	**43.** 11 * 11	**58.** 55 / 5
29. 6 * 7	**44.** 81 / 9	**59.** 63 / 9
30. 4 * 3	**45.** 8 * 8	**60.** 21 / 7
31. 14 / 2	**46.** 12 * 12	**61.** 15 * 3
32. 17 * 2	**47.** 16 / 4	**62.** 48 / 8
33. 12 * 10	**48.** 6 * 9	**63.** 9 * 8

Use with or after Lesson 1.9.

Write all of your answers on a separate sheet of paper.

Solve.

1. 322 + 921

2. 22 + 42 + 14

3. 540 + 191

4. 76.271 + 3.109

5. 6.152 + 8.019

6. 6.2 + 3.9 + 4.5

7. 16.5 + 97

8. 3.58 + 65.4

---

9. **Use the clues to complete the puzzle.**

    .

_3_ _9_ _6_ . _9_ _8_ _4_

- Add 43 and 23. Divide by 11 and write the result in the ones place.

- Triple the number in the ones place and divide by 2. Write the result in the tenths place.

- Multiply 8 ∗ 9. Subtract 68. Write the result in the thousandths place.

- Subtract the number in the tenths place from 57 and divide by 6. Write the result in the hundredths place.

- Divide 36 by the number in the thousandths place. Write the result in the tens place.

- Subtract the number in the ones place from the number in the tens place. Write the result in the hundreds place.

Write all of your answers on a separate sheet of paper.

Eight people are going to share $682 equally.

10. How many $100 bills does each person get?

11. How many dollars are left to share?

12. How many $10 bills does each person get?

13. How many dollars are left to share?

14. How many $1 bills does each person get?

15. How many dollars are left over?

16. If the leftover money is shared equally, how many cents does each person get?

17. Write a number model for the above problem.

Write the amounts.

18. (Q)(Q)(Q)(D)(D)(D)(N)(N)(P)(P)(P)(P)

19. | $1 | $1 | $1 | (Q)(D)(D)(D)(D)(N)
(P)(P)(P)

20. | $5 | $5 | $5 | $5 | $1 | (Q)(N)(N)

21. | $100 | $100 | $20 | $20 | $5 |
| $1 | $1 | (Q)

Fill in the missing numbers on the number lines.

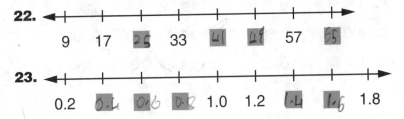

22. 9   17   25   33   41   49   57   65

23. 0.2   0.4   0.6   0.8   1.0   1.2   1.4   1.6   1.8

Practice Set 10

Write all of your answers on a separate sheet of paper.

Solve.

1. 7.49 − 6.65

2. 4.8 − 1.2

3. 819 − 742

4. 346 − 122

5. 5.32 − 4.59

6. 9,007 − 3,568

7. 47.9 − 10.7

8. 5,300 − 1,792

Read each statement. Tell if the measurement is *too small*, *OK*, or *too large*.

9. The book weighs 1 ton.

10. Ellen's sister is 5 yards tall.

11. The distance between San Francisco and Washington, D.C. is 115 miles.

12. The chicken weighs about 4 pounds.

13. The nickel weighs about 5 grams.

14. A mug holds about 1 liter of water.

15. Mr. Brown's shoe is about 13 centimeters long.

Complete the missing factors.

16. 70 * ■ = 210

17. ■ * 4 = 360

18. ■ * 8 = 640

19. 12 * ■ = 960

20. 400 * ■ = 3,600

21. ■ * 50 = 350

22. 9 * ■ = 810

23. ■ * 6 = 6,600

Write all of your answers on a separate sheet of paper.

Write a number sentence. Then find the solution.

1. The bakery sold 16 cherry pies and 21 strawberry pies. How many pies were sold in all?

2. Sue paid for lunch with a $10 bill. The tuna sandwich cost $2.49 and the orange juice cost $1.65. How much change did she receive?

3. Evan spent $35.72 on school supplies. Tanya spent $23.18. How much more did Evan spend than Tanya?

Estimate the total cost.

4. 10 rulers that cost 79¢ each

5. 8 scissors that cost $1.14 each

.6. 15 books that cost $2.35 each

7. 3 markers that cost $1.85 each

Answer the following questions.

8. How many sides does the polygon have?

9. What kind of polygon is shown?

10. If each side were 2.4 cm, what would the perimeter be?

11. How many lines of symmetry does it have?

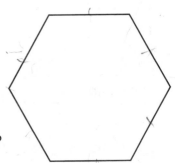

Write all of your answers on a separate sheet of paper.

12. Write the missing numbers. You may use a calculator.

Product	Exponential Notation	Standard Notation
5 * 5 * 5 * 5	5^4	625
8 * 8 * 8	■	■
■	10^5	■
■	■	144
13 * 13	■	■
■	■	400
■	25^4	■
30 * 30 * 30	■	■

Find the square numbers.

13. 9^2

14. 14^2

15. 20^2

16. 24^2

17. 32^2

18. 48^2

19. 65^2

20. 71^2

21. 100^2

Complete.

22. $2\frac{1}{2}$ hours = ■ minutes

23. 12 hours = ■ day

24. 2,700 seconds = ■ minutes

25. $10\frac{1}{2}$ days = ■ weeks

26. 365 days = ■ year

SRB
30 57
123

Write all of your answers on a separate sheet of paper.

Use the spinner for Items 1–4. Suppose you spin a paper clip on the base of the spinner 200 times. About how many times would you expect it to land on . . .

1. red? 75

2. blue? 50

3. yellow? 50

4. green? 25

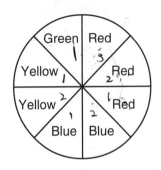

Write the digit in the hundredths place.

5. 2.15 **6.** 10.07 **7.** 3.142

8. 92.103 **9.** 7.13 **10.** 8.49

Write the fractional part for each picture.

Example  $\frac{2}{12}$ or $\frac{1}{6}$

11.  **12.**

13.  **14.**

Write all of your answers on a separate sheet of paper.

The following table shows the dates on which some recent presidents of the United States were sworn into office. It also shows each of their ages at the time they were sworn in.

President	Date Sworn In	Age
Ford	August 9, 1974	61
Carter	January 20, 1977	52
Reagan	January 20, 1981	69
Bush	January 20, 1989	64
Clinton	January 20, 1993	46

15. What is the mean (average) age of the presidents at the time they were sworn in?

16. Who was president for the shortest time?

17. Presidents are elected for a term of 4 years. Which presidents served more than 1 term?

18. Which of the presidents is the oldest today?

19. How much older was Carter when he was sworn in than Clinton when he was sworn in as President.

20. If President Ford was 61 when he was sworn in, how old was he on the same date in 1993?

Write all of your answers on a separate sheet of paper.

Round each number to the nearest hundred.

1. 659   **2.** 4,273   **3.** 94.42

4. 83,201   **5.** 16,495   **6.** 5,982

Round each number to the nearest hundredth.

7. 4.023   **8.** 15.617   **9.** 0.179

10. 6.005   **11.** 732.424   **12.** 95.189

Make a magnitude estimate for the product. Is the solution in the *tenths, ones, tens, hundreds, thousands,* or *ten-thousands*?

13. 21 * 37   **14.** 67 * 93

15. 0.5 * 4.2   **16.** 362 * 45

17. 1.2 * 0.8   **18.** 475 * 5.2

Solve.

19.
$$\begin{array}{r} 79 \\ +\ 356 \\ \hline 435 \end{array}$$

20.
$$\begin{array}{r} 2{,}256 \\ -\ 36 \\ \hline 2220 \end{array}$$

21.
$$\begin{array}{r} 120 \\ -\ 30 \\ \hline 90 \end{array}$$

22.
$$\begin{array}{r} 826 \\ +\ 182 \\ \hline 1008 \end{array}$$

23.
$$\begin{array}{r} 543 \\ +\ 768 \\ \hline 1311 \end{array}$$

24.
$$\begin{array}{r} 731 \\ +\ 610 \\ \hline 1341 \end{array}$$

Practice Set 14

Write all of your answers on a separate sheet of paper.

Solve.

1. 49 ∗ 53

2. 19 ∗ 247

3. 34 ∗ 4.7

4. 3.2 ∗ 9.7

5. 891 ∗ 127

6. 27.5 ∗ 16.8

7. 31 ∗ 346

8. 16.2 ∗ 97

Complete the "What's My Rule?" tables.

9.

Rule	in	out
out = in ∗ 30	6	180
	8	240
	9	
	11	
	15	

10.

Rule	in	out
~23	27	4
	33	10
		14
	24	
	51	28

11.

Rule	in	out
out = in + 8.5	15	
	23	
	6	
	41	
	122	

12.

Rule	in	out
out = in − 11	27	
	33	
		14
	24	
	39	28

Write all of your answers on a separate sheet of paper.

If 1 centimeter on a map represents 20 kilometers, then find the following:

13. 8 cm represents ▦ km.

14. 11 cm represents ▦ km.

15. 14 cm represents ▦ km.

16. 2.5 cm represents ▦ km.

17. 12 cm represents ▦ km.

Rewrite the number sentences with parentheses to make them correct.

18. $18 = 4 + 2 * 7$

19. $33 - 14 - 5 = 24$

20. $53 - 12 + 7 = 48$

21. $8 * 9 + 4 * 12 = 120$

22. $96 = 6 * 7 + 9$

23. $4 * 3 + 8 * 10 = 440$

24. $230 = 8 * 21 + 76 - 14$

25. $8 * 10 - 3 = 56$

Complete.

26. $10^2 = $ ▦

27. $9^▦ = 81$

28. $2 * 2 = 2^▦$

29. The square root of $121 = $ ▦

Write all of your answers on a separate sheet of paper.

Solve.

1. 61 * 24

2. 4.3 * 7

3. 92 * 1.37

4. 537 * 72

5. 18.3 * 6.5

6. 124 * 396

7. 4.15 * 2.7

8. 58 * 6.25

Tell whether each number is divisible by 3. Write *yes* or *no*.

9. 27   **10.** 78   **11.** 158   **12.** 682

Tell whether each number is divisible by 9. Write *yes* or *no*.

13. 36   **14.** 93   **15.** 117   **16.** 487

Solve.

17. ■ + 9 = 29

18. 300 + ■ = 500

19. 17 − ■ = 12

20. 100 − ■ = 75

21. 82 − ■ = 50

22. ■ + 92 = 108

23. ■ = 30 + 65

24. ■ − 60 = 55

25. 200 + ■ = 800

26. 170 − ■ = 90

Write all of your answers on a separate sheet of paper.

1. Use the clues to complete the puzzle.

1 5, 2 7 3, 6 4 9, 0 1 1

Find $\frac{1}{10}$ of 40. Double the result and write it in the thousands place.

Double 4. Divide the result by 2. Write the answer in the ten-thousands place.

Find 7 * 6. Reverse the digits in the result and divide by 8. Write the result in the millions place.

Add 6 to the digit in the thousands place. Divide by 7 and write the result in the hundred-millions place.

Write $\frac{12}{3}$ as a whole number in the ones place.

Subtract the number in the ones place from the number in the ten-thousands place. Write the result in the hundreds place.

Find $\frac{1}{3}$ of 18. Write the result in the hundred-thousands place.

Find 20% of 35. Write the result in the ten-millions place.

Add the number in the ten-millions place to the number in the hundred-millions place. Write the result in the ten-billions place.

Find $\frac{1}{8}$ of 8 and write the result in the tens place.

• Find the sum of all the digits in the chart so far. Subtract 39 from the result and write the answer in the billions place.

2. Write the number in words.

Write all of your answers on a separate sheet of paper.

Write the words for the following numbers.

3. 12,743,000

4. 8,054,000,000,000

5. 42,169,205,000,000

6. 16,802,946

To square a number, multiply the number by itself.

Complete.

7. $2^2 = $ ■

8. $4^■ = 16$

9. $5 * 5 = 5^■$

10. 8 squared = ■

Write the number models with parentheses and solve.

11. Add 73 to the difference of 2,465 and 846.

12. Subtract the sum of 224 and 613 from 2,548.

13. Add 72 to the difference of 3,527 and 1,565.

14. Subtract the sum of 128 and 27 from 228.

Mr. Henderson reported these scores on a quiz:
23, 18, 19, 23, 16, 12, 15, 12, 11, 16, 22, 19, 23

15. What is the maximum of the scores?

16. What is the minimum of the scores?

17. What is the range of the scores?

18. What is the mode of the scores?

19. What is the mean of the scores?

20. What is the median of the scores?

Write all of your answers on a separate sheet of paper.

Find the angle measures for the labeled angles. There are 360° in a circle and 180° in a straight line. Do not use a protractor.

1. m ∠G

2. m ∠H

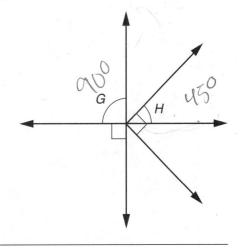

Write the letter of the best estimate for each problem.

3. 87 ∗ 3.6   **A.** 900

4. 2.87 ∗ 3.6   **B.** 2,000

5. 72 ∗ 58   **C.** 360

6. 879 ∗ 1.17   **D.** 12

7. 19.8 ∗ 132.5   **E.** 4,200

Solve.

8. 524
     − 154

9. 426
     − 273

10. 684
      + 27

11. 2,647
      − 235

12. 700
      − 480

13. 526
      + 203

Write all of your answers on a separate sheet of paper.

Write the letter of the measurement that best describes each angle. Do not use a protractor.

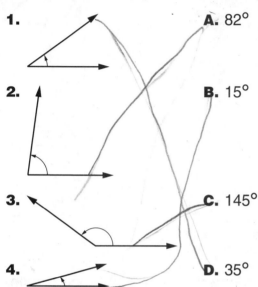

1.

A. 82°

2.

B. 15°

3.

C. 145°

4.

D. 35°

Write *true* or *false* for each number sentence.

5. 125 + 7 = 130

6. 23 * 6 > 100

7. 37.6 * 1.8 < 37.6

8. (5 * 2) + 18 = 41

9. 1.9 + 7.8 = 9.7

10. 1,600 ÷ 8 = 200

Round each number to the nearest hundredth.

11. 18.582

12. 5.826

13. 0.821

14. 634.624

15. 29.005

16. 23.205

Write all of your answers on a separate sheet of paper.

Rewrite the number sentences with parentheses to make them correct.

17. 7 * 12 − 6 = 42

18. 7 * 12 − 6 = 78

19. 230 − 130 − 50 = 150

20. 21 = 3 * 2.4 + 4.6

21. 3 * 8.3 + 5 * 12 = 84.9

22. 300 = 5 * 70 − 50

23. 4 * 10 + 6 − 1 = 60

24. 378 = 12 * 30 + 18

Use digits to write the following numbers.

25. nineteen billion, six hundred million

26. seventy-six million, twenty thousand, six hundred fourteen

27. six trillion, four hundred fifty billion

Complete the number lines.

28.

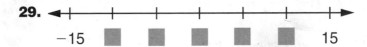

$\frac{1}{6}$ ▪ ▪ ▪ ▪ $\frac{6}{6}$ or 1

29.

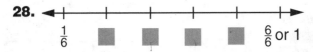

−15 ▪ ▪ ▪ ▪ ▪ 15

30.

$-\frac{1}{4}$ ▪ ▪ $\frac{1}{2}$ ▪ ▪ ▪

31.

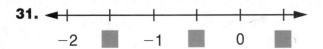

−2 ▪ −1 ▪ 0 ▪

32.

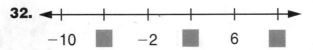

−10 ▪ −2 ▪ 6 ▪

Write all of your answers on a separate sheet of paper.

Write the name that describes each triangle:
equilateral, *isosceles*, or *scalene*.

1.

2.

3.
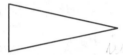

4.
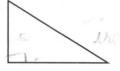

5.
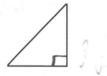

6.

Use the clues to find the number.

7. Clue 1: I am a prime number less than 30.
Clue 2: The sum of my digits is 5.

8. Clue 1: I am between 40 and 60.
Clue 2: I am divisible by 5.
Clue 3: The sum of my digits is 9.

9. Clue 1: I am greater than 500, but less than 1,000.
Clue 2: My square root is a square number.

Write all of your answers on a separate sheet of paper.

Write the letters of the names that fit the figure. More than one name may fit some figures.

1. 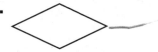   **A.** rhombus

2.    **B.** square

3. 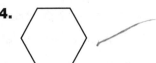   **C.** quadrangle

4.   **D.** hexagon

Write the letter of the prime factorization for each number.

5. 16   **A.** $2 * 2 * 2 * 5$

6. 40   **B.** $2 * 2 * 3 * 3$

7. 18   **C.** $2 * 2 * 2 * 2$

8. 36   **D.** $2 * 3 * 3$

Solve.

9. $24 = 6 * \blacksquare$ **10.** $8.2 + 9.8 = \blacksquare$

11. $9 * \blacksquare = \$1.80$ **12.** $\blacksquare / 1,700 = 5$

13. $82.4 - 12.8 = \blacksquare$ **14.** $180 * \blacksquare = 3,600$

15. $\blacksquare / 4.90 = 2$ **16.** $\$4.65 * 5 = \blacksquare$

Write all of your answers on a separate sheet of paper.

Susan, Antonio, Chris, Jonathan, and Julie went out to dinner. They ordered 3 pizzas. All 3 pizzas were the same size.

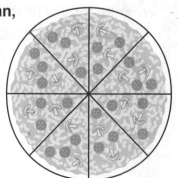

17. Susan and Julie shared one pizza. Susan ate $\frac{3}{8}$ of the pizza. Julie ate $\frac{1}{2}$ of the pizza. Who ate more?

18. How much of the pizza was left?

Antonio, Chris, and Jonathan shared the other two pizzas. Antonio ate $\frac{5}{8}$ of a pizza. Chris ate $\frac{3}{4}$ of a pizza. Jonathan ate $\frac{3}{6}$ of a pizza. Who ate more:

19. Chris or Antonio?

20. Chris or Jonathan?

21. Antonio or Jonathan?

22. Who ate the most?

23. How much was left?

24. How many slices were left from all 3 pizzas?

25. Susan, Antonio, Chris, Jonathan, and Julie want to share the remaining slices equally. How many sections should they divide the remaining slices into?

Use with or after Lesson 3.7.

Write all of your answers on a separate sheet of paper.

Write *acute, obtuse, right, straight,* or *reflex* to describe each angle.

1. Right

2. acute

3.  obtuse

4. reflex

5.  straight

6.  obtuse

---

Solve.

7. 900 / 90 = ■

8. 340 * 20 = ■

9. 1,200 = 120 * ■

10. 5 * 560 = ■

11. 40 * ■ = 6,000

12. ■ / 1,000 = 30

13. 2,800 / 700 = ■

14. 16 * ■ = 560

15. ■ / 70 = 10

16. 9 * 30 = ■

17. 2,200 / ■ = 11

18. 8 * 60 = ■

Complete.

19. 10^8 = ■

20. $10^■$ = 1,000,000,000

21. 10 * 10 * 10 * 10 * 10 * 10 * 10 = ■

22. 10 to the sixth power = ■

Write all of your answers on a separate sheet of paper.

Use the figures above to answer Items 1–4.

1. What fraction of the figures is represented by triangles?

2. What fraction of the figures is represented by polygons?

3. What fraction of the figures has at least 1 pair of parallel sides?

4. What fraction of the figures is not represented by quadrangles?

Find the missing angle measure. A triangle has 180°. Do not use a protractor.

5.

55°

90° ?

6.

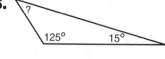

?

125°   15°

Copy the following numbers on your paper.

7. Underline the numbers that are divisible by 2. Circle the numbers that are divisible by 3. Cross out the numbers that are divisible by 5.

340   845   9,303   1,001   653

125   777   496   2,300   8,472

Write all of your answers on a separate sheet of paper.

In each set of problems below, do as many exercises as you can in one minute.

Problem Set 1	Problem Set 2	Problem Set 3
8. 7 * 1 7	**23.** 9 + 1 10	**38.** 9 * 5 45
9. 21 / 3 7	**24.** 15 − 8 7	**39.** 35 / 7 5
10. 28 / 7 4	**25.** 16 − 6 10	**40.** 8 + 2 10
11. 4 * 3 12	**26.** 7 + 7 14	**41.** 16 − 9 7
12. 18 / 6 3	**27.** 8 − 0 8	**42.** 8 * 5 40
13. 30 / 3 10	**28.** 6 + 7 13	**43.** 9 + 4 13
14. 5 * 0 0	**29.** 5 + 4 9	**44.** 81 / 9 9
15. 24 / 4 6	**30.** 9 + 7 16	**45.** 16 − 7 9
16. 30 / 5 6	**31.** 13 − 1 12	**46.** 15 − 6 9
17. 6 * 8 48	**32.** 12 − 7 5	**47.** 8 + 3 11
18. 10 * 6 60	**33.** 3 + 5 8	**48.** 7 * 9 63
19. 8 * 4 32	**34.** 10 − 7 3	**49.** 3 * 8 24
20. 54 / 9 6	**35.** 2 + 0 2	**50.** 72 / 8 9
21. 6 * 6 36	**36.** 16 − 8 8	**51.** 90 / 9 10
22. 56 / 7 8	**37.** 18 − 9 9	**52.** 7 + 4 11

Write all of your answers on a separate sheet of paper.

Use mental math to solve. Remember to break the number being divided into two or more friendly parts.

Example	Friendly parts:	Divide each part.
66 divided by 5	50 and 16	$50 \div 5 = 10$ $16 \div 5 = 3$ with 1 left over 66 divided by 5 equals 13 with 1 left over.

1. 71 divided by 3   **2.** 47 divided by 6

3. 87 divided by 8   **4.** 69 divided by 4

5. 95 divided by 7   **6.** 86 divided by 6

7. How many dots are in this array?

. . . .
. . . .
. . . .
. . . .

8. Write a number model for the array.

9. How many dots are in this array?

. . . .
. . . .
. . . .
. . . .
. . . .

10. Write a number model for the array.

Complete.

11. $10^4 = \blacksquare$ **12.** $5^{\blacksquare} = 25$

13. $10{,}000{,}000 = 10^{\blacksquare}$ **14.** $3^{\blacksquare} = 27$

15. $64 = 4^{\blacksquare}$ **16.** $\blacksquare^4 = 81$

Write all of your answers on a separate sheet of paper.

Write the value of the digit 8 in the numerals below.

17. 589,000

18. 87,402,000,000

19. 312,719,538

20. 482,391,092

21. 328,946,326

22. What kind of polygon is shown below?

23. If each side were 6.9 centimeters, what would the perimeter be?

Complete the number lines.

24.

4.5   5.2

25.

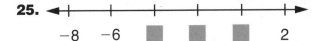

−8   −6   2

26.

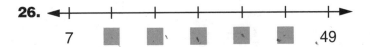

7   .49

27.

3   123

Write all of your answers on a separate sheet of paper.

Divide.

1. 518 / 5   **2.** 183 ÷ 6

3. 464 ÷ 4   **4.** 630 / 8

5. 967 / 9   **6.** 1,344 / 12

7. 6,568 ÷ 8   **8.** 3,068 ÷ 23

9. Ellen had 293 buttons. She places 6 buttons in each bag. How many bags of buttons can she make?

Tell whether each number is even or odd. Then list all of the factors.

10. 49   **11.** 62   **12.** 76

Write the amounts.

13. Ⓠ Ⓠ Ⓓ Ⓓ Ⓓ Ⓝ Ⓝ
Ⓟ Ⓟ Ⓟ Ⓟ Ⓟ Ⓟ Ⓟ

14. $1 $1 $1 Ⓠ Ⓓ Ⓓ Ⓓ Ⓝ Ⓟ Ⓟ

15. $5 $1 $1 Ⓠ Ⓠ Ⓠ Ⓝ Ⓝ

16. $100 $20 $20 $5 $1 $1 $1

Write all of your answers on a separate sheet of paper.

Use the map and map scale to answer the questions.

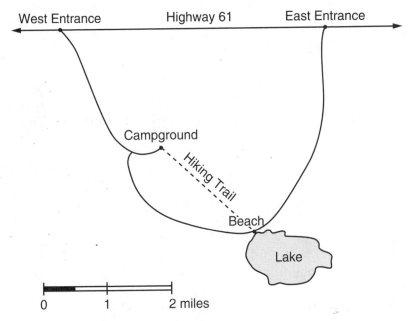

1. How far is it from the East Entrance to the lake?

2. Which is closer to the beach, the East or West Entrance?

3. Which entrance is closer to the campground? By how many miles?

4. Sue and Jason want to go from the campground to the beach. If Sue rides her bike on the road at 5 miles per hour, and Jason walks on the trail at 3 miles per hour, who will reach the beach first?

5. If there were a trail around the lake, estimate how long this trail would be.

6. If you wanted to hike about 4 miles, describe a route you might take.

Write all of your answers on a separate sheet of paper.

Write the numbers in order from least to greatest.

7. 1.79, 0.12, 5.1, 0.4, 4.03

8. 9.8, 0.98, 8.09, 8.9, 0.89

9. 0.2, 2.2, 0.12, 1.2, 0.21

Estimate the answer to each multiplication problem.

10. 185 $*$ 22   **11.** 92 $*$ 41

12. 781 $*$ 68   **13.** 209 $*$ 71

14. 314 $*$ 18   **15.** 903 $*$ 47

Solve.

16. 900 $*$ 800 $= p$ **17.** 5,000 $* d = 300{,}000$

18. 5,400 $= x * 90$ **19.** 42,000 $= 700 * s$

20. 3 $* 1{,}500 = n$ **21.** 64,000 / 8,000 $= g$

Solve.

22. A mole can dig a tunnel 300 feet long in one night. How many yards can a mole dig in three weeks? (Reminder: 3 ft = 1 yd)

23. A bottle-nosed dolphin can dive to a depth of 3,000 feet in 2 minutes. About how many yards per second is that?

24. When it snows, Shawn charges $4 for every sidewalk he shovels, and $5 for every driveway he shovels. If he shovels 8 sidewalks and 3 driveways, how much does he earn?

Write all of your answers on a separate sheet of paper.

Make a magnitude estimate of the quotient. Is the solution in the *tenths, ones, tens,* or *hundreds?* Then divide.

1. $18.9 \div 7$

2. $297 \div 5$

3. $61.6 / 4$

4. $25.2 / 6$

5. $\$40.43 \div 3$

6. $786 / 6$

Solve.

7. $623 + 812$

8. $170 - 68$

9. $495 - 381$

10. $2{,}791 + 342$

11. $3{,}465 + 1{,}273$

12. $7{,}514 - 2{,}356$

Write a number sentence. Then find the solution.

13. There are 17 cards in each box. On the shelf are 9 boxes. How many cards are on the shelf?

14. The library is open 6 days a week. Each day an average of 430 books are checked out. What is the average total number of books that are checked out in a week?

15. Karen bought a jacket for $\$42.59$ and a pair of slacks for $\$23.65$. How much did she spend in all?

Write all of your answers on a separate sheet of paper.

Write a number sentence, then solve. Tell what you did about the remainder.

1. 437 students need calculators. Calculators come in boxes of 12. How many boxes of calculators need to be ordered so that each student will have a calculator?

2. Mrs. Woods has 27 feet of fabric. She needs to make 4 identical costumes. How much fabric does she have for each costume?

3. Oscar is making fruit baskets. Each fruit basket must have 15 pieces of fruit. How many baskets can he make with 123 pieces of fruit?

Rewrite the number sentences with parentheses to make them correct.

4. $42 * 8 - 5 = 126$

5. $9.5 = 6.3 + 6.4 / 2$

6. $260 - 240 - 6 = 26$

7. $10 - 12 + 9 = -11$

8. $8 * 6 + 9 * 5 = 600$

9. $170 = 20 * 4 + 90$

10. $7 * 4 + 10 * 13 = 158$

11. $115.8 = 11.6 * 3 + 9 * 9$

Write all of your answers on a separate sheet of paper.

Measure each angle to the nearest degree.

12.

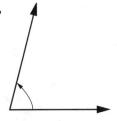

13.

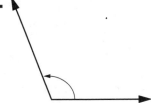

Write the digits for the following numbers.

14. one hundred sixty-two and nine hundred seventy-four thousandths

15. sixteen and one hundred forty-seven thousandths

16. eleven and three hundred seventy-one thousandths

17. one thousand and forty-two thousandths

18. sixteen and four hundred seven thousandths

Write the words for the following numbers.

19. 171.603

20. 34.087

21. 1.042

22. 71.627

23. 84.829

Write all of your answers on a separate sheet of paper.

1. How many pieces of fruit are there?

2. What fraction of the group is represented by apples?

3. What fraction of the group is represented by pears?

4. What fraction of the group is represented by bananas?

5. What fraction of the group is represented by oranges?

Write *true* or *false* for each number sentence.

6. $15 \div 3 < 16 \div 4$ **7.** $2.93 - 1.05 = 2.43$

8. $96 - (2 * 3) = 40 + 50$ **9.** $375 \div 25 = 15$

10. $17 + 23 = 100 / 2$ **11.** $0.5 * 6 = 6$

Measure each line segment to nearest centimeter.

12. ———————————————

13. ———————————————————

Write all of your answers on a separate sheet of paper.

Solve.

14. 32.76
+ 13.98

4 6.7 4

15. 3.187
+ 1.290

4.477

16. 547.2
− 371.9

1 75.3

17. 30)180

18. 6)4.2

19. 9)103.5

20. 8,323
+ 1,475

21. 5,335
+ 3,182

22. 82,416
+ 15,249

23. A parking lot has 4 rows.
Each row has spaces for
11 cars. How many cars
can be parked in this lot?

44 cars

24. Write a number model for the above problem.

Fill in the missing numbers on the number lines.

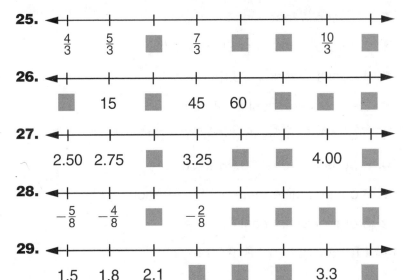

25. $\frac{4}{3}$ $\frac{5}{3}$ ■ $\frac{7}{3}$ ■   ■ $\frac{10}{3}$ ■

26. ■   15   ■   45   60   ■   ■   ■

27. 2.50   2.75   ■   3.25   ■   ■   4.00   ■

28. $-\frac{5}{8}$ $-\frac{4}{8}$ ■ $-\frac{2}{8}$ ■   ■   ■   ■

29. 1.5   1.8   2.1   ■   ■   ■   3.3   ■

Write all of your answers on a separate sheet of paper.

The circle at the right is $\frac{8}{8}$ or 1.
Write the mixed number for
each diagram.

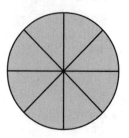

1.  **2.**

3. 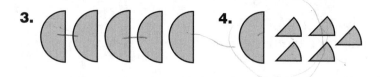 **4.**

Find the total cost of each of the following.

5. 18 pencils that cost 14¢ each

6. 7 scissors that cost $0.68 each

7. 4 books that cost $3.58 each

8. 28 rulers that cost $1.23 each

9. 2 pairs of shoes that cost $15.59 each

10. 8 pens that cost $0.98 each

11. 6 cans of juice that cost $4.24 each

12. 5 oranges that cost $0.20 each

13. 11 hats that cost $19.99 each

Use with or after Lesson 5.2.

Write all of your answers on a separate sheet of paper.

Find the amounts.

14. (Q)(Q)(Q)(Q)(Q)(D)(D)(N)(N)(P)(P)(P)

15. | $1 | $1 | $1 | (Q)(D)(D)(D)(D)(P)(P)

16. | $5 | $5 | $5 | $5 | $5 | $1 |
(Q)(N)(N)

17. | $100 | $100 | $20 | $20 | $5 | $1 | $1 |

Answer the following.

18. What is the prime factorization for 42?

2 * 3 * 7   3 * 7 * 7

2 * 2 * 7   3 * 7

19. What is the prime factorization for 80?

2 * 4 * 5   2 * 2 * 2 * 2 * 5

2 * 2 * 2 * 3 * 5   5 * 5 * 2 * 2 * 2

20. What is the prime factorization for 34?

2 * 3 * 5   2 * 2 * 2 * 3

2 * 17   2 * 2 * 3 * 3

21. What is the prime factorization for 48?

2 * 5 * 5   2 * 2 * 2 * 2 * 3

2 * 23   2 * 2 * 2 * 3 * 3

Write all of your answers on a separate sheet of paper.

Write two equivalent fractions for each given fraction.

1. $\frac{2}{3}$ **2.** $\frac{5}{6}$ **3.** $\frac{9}{12}$

4. $\frac{4}{16}$ **5.** $\frac{3}{10}$ **6.** $\frac{1}{5}$

Write the fractions in order from least to greatest.

7. $\frac{7}{12}, \frac{1}{12}, \frac{3}{12}, \frac{8}{12}, \frac{11}{12}$

8. $\frac{3}{6}, \frac{3}{5}, \frac{3}{4}, \frac{3}{9}, \frac{3}{12}$

9. $\frac{1}{4}, \frac{1}{8}, \frac{3}{16}, \frac{5}{8}, \frac{7}{16}$

Write the number sentences with parentheses and solve.

10. Add 36 to the difference of 229 and 74.

11. Subtract the sum of 23 and 56 from 312.

12. Add 18 to the difference of 260 and 176.

13. Subtract the sum of 76 and 41 from 189.

Complete the number lines.

14.

4   634

15.

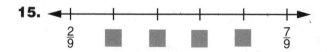

$\frac{2}{9}$ $\frac{7}{9}$

16.

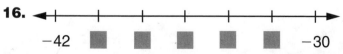

−42   −30

Use with or after Lesson 5.3.

Write all of your answers on a separate sheet of paper.

Rename the shaded part of the square as a fraction and a decimal.

1.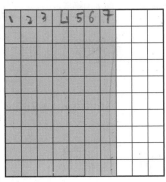

2.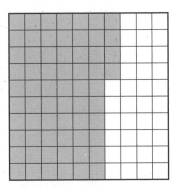

3.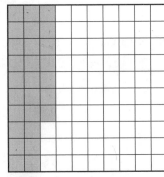

4.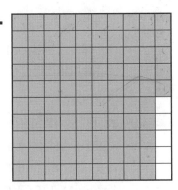

5.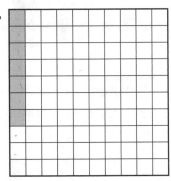

6.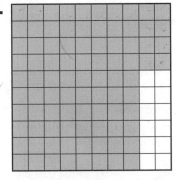

Write all of your answers on a separate sheet of paper.

Use the map and map scale to answer the questions below.

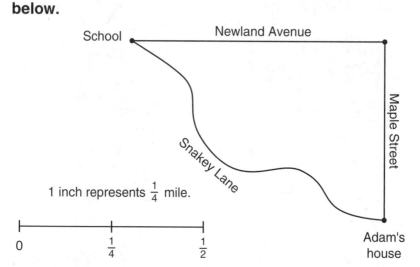

7. About how far would Adam have walked from school once he reached the corner of Newland and Maple?

8. About how far would Adam have walked if he had taken Snakey Lane home?

9. If Adam walked at a rate of 2.5 miles per hour on Snakey Lane, and a bus took 25 minutes to get to his house, which means is faster? By how many minutes?

10. If Adam's mother jogged down Snakey Lane from the house to the school and came back along Newland Avenue and Maple Street, how far would she have jogged?

11. If Adam lived on Maple Street, halfway between Snakey Lane and Newland Avenue, which route would be shorter?

Write all of your answers on a separate sheet of paper.

1. Write the missing numbers for the table.

Fraction	Decimal	Percent
$\frac{50}{100}$	0.5	50%
$\frac{100}{3}$	33.3	$33\frac{1}{3}\%$
$\frac{6}{10}$	0.6	60%
$\frac{32}{100}$	0.32	32%

Round to the nearest hundredth.

2. 14.096

3. 3.746

4. 2.149

5. 23.692

6. 4.385

7. 5.001

Write the coordinates of the points on the coordinate grid.

8. *A*

9. *B*

10. *C*

11. *D*

12. *E*

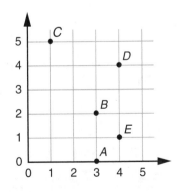

13. Using the same coordinate grid, write the coordinates that would be on the same line as points *B* and *D*.

Write all of your answers on a separate sheet of paper.

Solve.

14.   63
    * 36

15.   95
    * 26

16.   67
    * 25

17.   17
    * 57

18. 34,344
    − 3,640

19.   80
    * 17

20.   387
    + 3,643

21.   40
    * 70

22. 4,751
    − 800

23.   760
    * 32

24.   52
    * 19

25.   75
    * 23

Write the amounts.

26. 3 | $1 |, 1 (Q), 3 (D), 1 (P)

27. 3 | $5 |, 2 | $1 |, 1 (Q), 3 (N)

28. 2 | $100 |, 2 | $20 |, 1 | $5 |, 3 | $1 |

29. 7 (Q), 2 (D), 3 (N), 3 (P)

30. 10 (Q), 12 (D), 18 (N), 16 (P)

31. 12 | $1 |, 16 (Q), 44 (N)

Write the next three numbers in the pattern.

32. 18;   1,800;   180,000

33. 53,   67,   81

34. 19,   8,   −3

35. 0.75,   15,   300

Write all of your answers on a separate sheet of paper.

Write the decimal as a fraction or a mixed number.

1. 0.7   **2.** 0.3   **3.** 1.5

4. 4.2   **5.** 2.9   **6.** 2.7

Write *yes* if the fractions are equivalent. Write *no* if they are not.

7. $\frac{10}{12}, \frac{5}{6}$ **8.** $\frac{5}{10}, \frac{2}{3}$

9. $\frac{3}{21}, \frac{1}{7}$ **10.** $\frac{9}{24}, \frac{3}{8}$

11. $\frac{2}{6}, \frac{3}{5}$ **12.** $\frac{2}{5}, \frac{10}{15}$

13. $\frac{14}{20}, \frac{2}{7}$ **14.** $\frac{3}{12}, \frac{12}{48}$

Find the perimeter of each shape.

15. 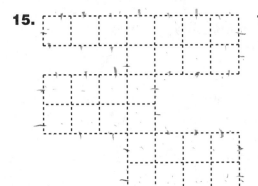   **16.**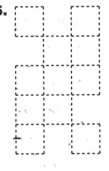

Write all of your answers on a separate sheet of paper.

Find the landmarks for the data shown on the graph.

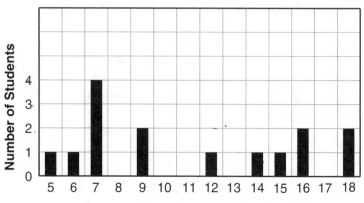

Number of Pages Read by Each Student

1. minimum 5

2. maximum 18

3. range 13

4. mode

5. mean

6. median

Complete the "What's My Rule?" tables.

7.

Rule	in	out
out = in / 25	300	
	475	
	825	
		17
	160	

8.

Rule	in	out
out = in / 9	270	
	81	
		14
	117	
		21

Solve.

9. $636 - x = 85$

10. $15.9 + 38.5 = t$

11. $152 + 652 = p$

12. $847 - 264 = d$

Write all of your answers on a separate sheet of paper.

Examine the circle graph and answer the questions below.

Favorite Sports

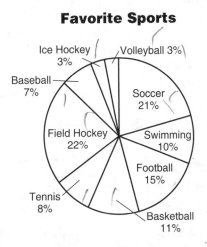

1. Which is the favorite sport of students in this survey?
2. Which is more popular, tennis or baseball?
3. About how many times more popular is field hockey than swimming?
4. How many times more popular is soccer than ice hockey?
5. What percent of the students like sports that use a spherical ball?
6. What percent of the students like sports in which you hit a ball?
7. What percent of the students like sports in which you throw a ball?
8. What percent of the students like sports that can be played outside?
9. About how many times more popular is football than tennis?

Write all of your answers on a separate sheet of paper.

Susana made 12 of 16 shots in the basketball game.

10. What fraction of the shots did she make?

11. What percent of the shots did she make?

12. At this rate, how many shots would she make if she took 20 shots?

Mr. Ryan set a goal of running a total of 100 miles each month. He filled in the squares on the grid at right to keep track of the miles he ran. Each square represents 1 mile.

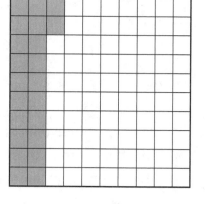

13. How many miles has Mr. Ryan run so far this month?

14. What fraction of 100 miles did he run so far?

15. What percent of his goal has he reached?

16. If it took him 10 days to run this many miles, do you think he will reach his goal?

17. About how many miles should he run each day in an average month in order to reach his goal?

18. About how many miles will he need to run the rest of the days in this month in order to reach his goal?

Write all of your answers on a separate sheet of paper.

The graph below shows the number of books students read, outside of school, in one month.

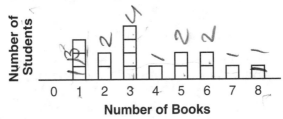

Number of Students

Number of Books

1. What is the minimum number of books?

2. What is the maximum?   **3.** What is the median?

4. What is the mean?   **5.** What is the mode?

Solve.

6. 2,940
+ 185

7. 59
* 28

8. 7,474
+ 2,852

9. 2,058
− 1,744

10. 10,769
+ 2,375

11. 63
* 36

12. 4.928
− 1.878

13. 2.564
− 1.9

14. 9.375
+ 2.058

Complete.

15. 6 ft = ■ in.   **16.** 2 yd = ■ ft

17. 14 ft 3 in. = ■ in.   **18.** 7 yd 4 ft = ■ ft

19. 76 in. = ■ ft ■ in.   **20.** 28 ft = ■ yd ■ ft

21. 3,160 in. = ■ yd ■ ft ■ in.

Use with or after Lesson 6.1.

57

Write all of your answers on a separate sheet of paper.

Measure each line segment to the nearest millimeter.

1. ———

2. —————

3. ————

4. ——

---

5. Use the clues to complete the puzzle.

- Multiply 6 ∗ 40. Subtract 233 and write the result in the ones place.

- Write 75% of 4 in the hundredths place.

- Find $\frac{1}{20}$ of 100. Write the result in the thousandths place.

- Add 5 to the number in the hundredths place. Write the result in the tenths place.

Copy the numbers given for 6–13. Then <u>circle</u> the numbers that are divisible by 2 AND 3.

6. 3,411   **7.** 3,846   **8.** 8,036   **9.** 552

10. 9,992   **11.** 144   **12.** 603   **13.** 7,212

List all the factors of each number.

14. 42   **15.** 15   **16.** 38   **17.** 28

Write all of your answers on a separate sheet of paper.

Use the information in the stem-and-leaf plot to answer items 1–4.

1. How many scores are reported on the stem-and-leaf plot?

2. What is the maximum?

3. What is the minimum?

4. What is the median?

Science Test Scores

Stems (10s)	Leaves (1s)
2	7 7 8
3	1 3 3 5 6 8 8 9
4	0 0 1 2 3 3 3 3 4 5 7
5	0 0

Tell whether each triangle is *equilateral, isosceles,* or *scalene.*

5.

6.

7.

8.

Compare. Write < or >.

9. 265,168 ■ 29,518

10. 51,462 ■ 54,169

11. 1,645,283 ■ 1,644,823

12. 22,469,743 ■ 22,567,843

Write all of your answers on a separate sheet of paper.

Solve.

13. 65 * 65

14. 345 / 15

15. 835 * 3

16. 1,500 / 25

17. 23 * 25

18. 169 / 13

19. 39 * 2

20. 650 / 9

> 1 gallon = 4 quarts = 16 cups

21. A good milking cow will give up to 6,000 quarts of milk in a year. How many gallons is that?

22. About how many gallons is that per day?

23. If a family uses 2 gallons of milk per week, how many cups of milk does the family consume in a year?

Make name-collection boxes for the numbers below. Use as many different numbers and operations as you can.

Example

419.641
420 − 0.359
$419 + \frac{641}{1000}$
419,641 / 1,000
400 + 19.641

24. 3.805

25. 21.87

26. 8.925

27. 392.8

Write all of your answers on a separate sheet of paper.

Examine the mystery plots below.

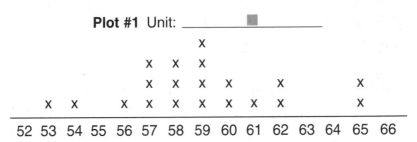

Plot #1 Unit: _____ ▦ _____

```
                    X
            X   X   X
            X   X   X   X       X           X
    X   X       X   X   X   X   X   X   X       X
```
52 53 54 55 56 57 58 59 60 61 62 63 64 65 66

Plot #2 Unit: _____ ▦ _____

```
        X
        X   X   X   X       X
   X      X X    X X X   X X X   X   X   X   X   X           X
```
26 28 30 32 34 36 38 40 42 44 46 48 50 52 54

---

1. Which graph could describe the ages of fifth graders' mothers?

2. Which graph could describe the ages of people retiring from a business?

In the numeral 7,128,490,563 the 8 stands for 8,000,000.

3. What does the 7 stand for?

4. What does the 1 stand for?

5. What does the 0 stand for?

6. What does the 9 stand for?

7. What does the 2 stand for?

8. What does the 4 stand for?

Write all of your answers on a separate sheet of paper.

Write the digit in the hundredths place.

9. 5.392   **10.** 3.731   **11.** 0.027

12. 1.856   **13.** 8.374   **14.** 702.6152

Write the next three numbers in the pattern.

15. 60, 180, 300

16. 9, 15, 21

17. $\frac{6}{4}, \frac{5}{4}, \frac{4}{4}$

Write the amounts.

18. | $1 | $1 | (Q)(D)(N)(N)(N)(N)(P)

19. | $5 | $5 | $5 | $5 | $5 | $5 | $1 |
| $1 | $1 | $1 | (Q)(Q)(N)

20. | $100 | $20 | $20 | $20 | $5 | $1 |
(Q)(Q)(Q)

---

21. Measure the sides of the shape to the nearest $\frac{1}{10}$ cm.

■ cm

■ cm

22. What is its perimeter?

Use with or after Lesson 6.4.

Write all of your answers on a separate sheet of paper.

Add or subtract.

1. $\frac{1}{3} + \frac{1}{3}$

2. $2\frac{1}{10} + \frac{3}{10}$

3. $\frac{7}{8} - \frac{2}{8}$

4. $3\frac{1}{2} + \frac{1}{2}$

5. $\frac{15}{16} - \frac{7}{16}$

6. $2\frac{5}{6} - \frac{11}{6}$

7. $\frac{2}{5} + \frac{2}{5}$

8. $9\frac{7}{12} - 2\frac{5}{12}$

Solve.

9. 826
 $-\ 104$

10. 930
 $-\ 285$

11. 962
 $+\ 268$

12. $2,965$
 $-\ 1,583$

13. $1,903$
 $-\ 825$

14. $2,532$
 $+\ 7,378$

15. 962
 $+\ 25$

16. $2,682$
 $-\ 632$

17. $1,523$
 $+\ 1,497$

18. Find the perimeter of each regular polygon.

Regular Polygon	Length of 1 side	Perimeter
square	15 cm	▪
pentagon	5.1 cm	▪
hexagon	$4\frac{1}{2}$ cm	▪
octagon	2.02 cm	▪

Write all of your answers on a separate sheet of paper.

Use clock fractions, if helpful, to solve these problems. Write each answer as a fraction.

1. $\frac{5}{12} + \frac{5}{12}$

2. $\frac{1}{4} + \frac{1}{3}$

3. $\frac{5}{6} - \frac{1}{6}$

4. $\frac{11}{12} - \frac{1}{12}$

5. $\frac{3}{4} + \frac{1}{6}$

6. $\frac{5}{6} + \frac{1}{12}$

7. $\frac{2}{3} - \frac{1}{4}$

8. $\frac{5}{6} - \frac{1}{3}$

9. $\frac{1}{6} + \frac{1}{6}$

10. $\frac{13}{12} - \frac{5}{12}$

Write the number sentences with parentheses and solve.

11. Add 5.43 to the difference of 10.15 and 7.93.

12. Subtract the sum of 6 and 1.35 from 7.75.

13. Add 39 to the difference of 17.00 and 6.47.

14. Subtract the sum of 81 and 8.92 from 848.37.

Solve.

15. How many 12s in 2,400?

16. How many 70s in 8,400?

17. How many 1,000s in 10^6?

18. 16 * 80

19. 84 * 50

20. 600 * 8.3

21. 29.3 * 9

Write all of your answers on a separate sheet of paper.

The pizza shown has been cut into 12 equal slices.

M = mushroom
P = pepperoni
S = sausage
O = onion

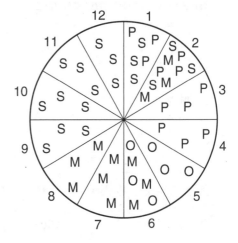

22. Write a decimal to show the part of the pizza that has just one topping.

23. What percent of the pizza has 2 or more toppings?

24. What fraction of the slices has only sausage?

25. What fraction of the pizza has no onions?

26. If all the slices with mushrooms are eaten first, how many slices are left?

27. What fraction of the remaining slices has pepperoni?

28. What percent of the pizza has only vegetables?

29. What fraction of the pizza has only meat?

30. Joe and Trish eat all the slices with sausage. Write a fraction to show the part of the pizza that is left for Adam, Carrie, and Dave to share.

31. If the three share the leftover pizza equally, how many slices should each one get?

Write all of your answers on a separate sheet of paper.

Rewrite each pair of fractions as equivalent fractions with a common denominator.

1. $\frac{2}{3}, \frac{3}{4}$

2. $\frac{3}{5}, \frac{1}{2}$

3. $\frac{2}{5}, \frac{1}{3}$

4. $\frac{5}{6}, \frac{4}{5}$

5. $\frac{1}{2}, \frac{2}{3}$

6. $\frac{3}{7}, \frac{2}{3}$

7. $\frac{1}{3}, \frac{3}{10}$

8. $\frac{2}{5}, \frac{3}{7}$

Write each fraction as a percent.

9. $\frac{7}{10}$

10. $\frac{6}{100}$

11. $\frac{1}{2}$

12. $\frac{3}{4}$

13. $\frac{2}{5}$

14. $\frac{3}{20}$

Make a magnitude estimate for the quotient. Is the solution in the *tenths, ones, tens,* or *hundreds?*

15. 629 / 9

16. 32.1 / 6

17. 1.62 / 7

18. $86.16 / 5

19. 678.1 / 4

20. 885 / 21

21. 239 / 35

22. 4.72 / 6

Write all of your answers on a separate sheet of paper.

Complete.

23. $3^3 = $ ■

24. $4^■ = 64$

25. $8 * 8 * 8 * 8 = $ ■

26. 6 to the fourth power $= $ ■

27. The square root of ■ $= 11$

Rewrite the number sentences with parentheses to make them correct.

28. $8 * 10 - 5 = 75$　　**29.** $6 * 18 - 6 = 72$

30. $42 - 21 - 7 = 14$　　**31.** $18 - 24 - 7 = 1$

32. $5 * 8 + 2 * 13 = 650$　**33.** $117 = 9 * 8 + 5$

34. $236 = 4 * 8 + 51$　　**35.** $448 = 7 * 22 + 47 - 5$

Solve.

36. How many 80s in 400?

37. How many 110s in 7,700?

38.　　12
　　　$* 2,100$

39.　　41
　　　$* 60$

40.　　119
　　　$* 3$

41.　153
　　　$* 5$

42.　286
　　　$* 23$

43.　　56
　　　$* 15$

44.　820
　　　$* 16$

45. $26\overline{)364}$

46. $6\overline{)312}$

Practice Set 43

Write all of your answers on a separate sheet of paper.

Write the letter of the number that matches the expression.

1. $6 * 6 * 6$ **A.** 15,625

2. $5 * 10^5$ **B.** 8,000,000

3. 5^6 **C.** 500,000

4. $3^2 * 4^3$ **D.** 216

5. 3 to the seventh power   **E.** 576

6. $8 * 10^6$ **F.** 2,187

Complete the "What's My Rule?" tables.

7.

Rule: out = in / 30	in	out
	180	
	240	
	990	
	1,260	
	1,500	

8.

Rule	in	out
	43	4
	33	−6
		14
	24	
	71	32

9.

Rule: out = in * 105	in	out
	6	630
	8	
		945
	11	
	15	

10.

Rule	in	out
	54	9
	30	5
		6
	1	
	2	

Use with or after Lesson 7.2.

Write all of your answers on a separate sheet of paper.

11. Use the clues to complete the puzzle.

___ ___ ___, ___ ___ ___, ___ ___ ___, ___ ___ ___

- Find $\frac{2}{5}$ of 20. Write the result in the thousands place.

- Add 1 to the number in the thousands place. Write the answer in the ten-thousands place.

- Find 14 * 4. Reverse the digits in the result and divide by 13. Write the result in the millions place.

- Add 6 to the digit in the ten-thousands place. Divide by 5 and write the result in the hundred-thousands place.

- Write $\frac{14}{2}$ as a whole number in the hundred-millions place.

- Find 60% of 10. Write the result in the ten-millions place.

- Subtract 3 from the number in the hundred-millions place. Write the result in the ten-billions place.

- Find $\frac{3}{7}$ of 49. Subtract 19 and write the result in the hundred-billions place.

- Find the sum of all the digits in the chart so far. Divide the result by 44 and write the answer in the billions place.

- Write 0 in the remaining places.

12. Write the number in words.

Practice Set 44

Write all of your answers on a separate sheet of paper.

Write each number using scientific notation.

1. 6 million

2. 20,000

3. 500,000

4. 100 billion

5. 40,000,000

6. 9 trillion

7. 3 thousand

8. 80 million

Write the numbers in order from least to greatest.

9. 1 million; $3 * 10^4$; 4 thousand; 100,000; $4 * 10^5$

10. $6 * 10^5$; 2 million, 160,000; $5 * 10 * 10 * 10$; 25 thousand

11. 33,000,000; $9 * 10^6$; 17 million; 1 billion; 4,000,000,000,000

Solve.

12. 236
     $* 43$

13.   25
     $* 35$

14. 235
     $* 85$

15. 35,235
     $+ 745$

16. 345
     $+ 89$

17. 55,000
     $+ 4,500$

18. 5,233
     $- 3,407$

19. 435
     $- 105$

20. 516
     $+ 242$

Use with or after Lesson 7.3.

Write all of your answers on a separate sheet of paper.

Rewrite the number models with parentheses to make them correct.

1. $28 / 4 - 7 = 0$

2. $23.2 = 8 * 3 - 0.8$

3. $129 - 18 - 48 = 63$

4. $57.6 = 3 * 12.8 + 6.4$

5. $11 * 4.2 + 6 * 10.1 = 106.8$

6. $-70 = 7 * 50 - 60$

7. $13 * 14 + 8 - 3 = 187$

Write the letter of the prime factorization for each number.

8. 70	**a.** $2 * 3 * 5$	**b.** $2 * 5 * 7$
9. 29	**a.** $1 * 29$	**b.** $2 * 5 * 19$
10. 80	**a.** $2^5 * 4$	**b.** $2^4 * 5$
11. 28	**a.** $2 * 2 * 7$	**b.** $2^3 * 72$

Write each fraction in simplest form.

12. $\frac{24}{4}$ **13.** $\frac{36}{12}$ **14.** $\frac{11}{11}$ **15.** $\frac{70}{10}$

16. $\frac{48}{8}$ **17.** $\frac{18}{3}$ **18.** $\frac{6}{4}$ **19.** $\frac{8}{1}$

20. $\frac{9}{12}$ **21.** $\frac{40}{80}$ **22.** $\frac{14}{16}$ **23.** $\frac{24}{38}$

Use with or after Lesson 7.4.

Write all of your answers on a separate sheet of paper.

Write *true* or *false* for each number sentence. Follow the rules of order for operations.

1. $(3 + 5) * 4 = 32$

2. $(18 - 6) * 2 - 3 = 24$

3. $(48 - 2^2) \div 10 = 5$

4. $15 - 4 * 2 + 1 = 8$

5. $100 \div (25 + 25) + 25 = 27$

6. $16 - (8 + 2) = 10$

Identify each angle. Write *acute, right, obtuse,* or *straight.*

7.

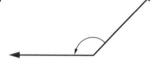

8.

9.

10.

Solve. Write each answer as a mixed number.

11. $172 \div 8$

12. $367 \div 12$

13. $431 \div 6$

14. $572 \div 3$

Write all of your answers on a separate sheet of paper.

Write the digit in the thousandths place.

15. 5.967   **16.** 1.2350   **17.** 8.84256

18. 0.47000   **19.** 3.368   **20.** 10.96733

Solve.

21. $360 - z = 241$

22. $34 + 23 = y$

23. $646 + 324 = n$

24. $980 - 150 = x$

25. $2,350 - m = 1,982$

26. $90 = 10,800 / p$

27. 478
    $- 55$

28. 363
    $- 67$

29. 34
    $* 9$

30. 3,436
    $+ 2,436$

31. 3,456
    $* 63$

32. $16\overline{)384}$

33. An elephant can eat 500 pounds of hay and drink 60 gallons of water in one day. About how many pounds of hay would an elephant eat in a week?

34. About how many pounds of hay does an elephant eat in a year?

35. How many gallons of water does an elephant drink in one year?

36. A box of pinwheel cookies contains 42 cookies. Richard and his six friends share the cookies equally. How many does each get?

Write all of your answers on a separate sheet of paper.

Write the letter that identifies each number on the number line.

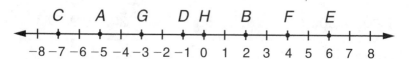

1. −1   **2.** 4   **3.** 0   **4.** 6

5. −7   **6.** 2   **7.** −3   **8.** −5

Compare. Write >, <, or =.

9. $-10 \ \blacksquare\ 4\frac{1}{2}$ **10.** $-3 \ \blacksquare\ -5$

11. $-3.5 \ \blacksquare\ -3\frac{1}{2}$ **12.** $-7 \ \blacksquare\ 3$

13. $-2\frac{1}{2} \ \blacksquare\ -2\frac{1}{4}$ **14.** $6\frac{1}{2} \ \blacksquare\ -3\frac{1}{3}$

Complete the number lines.

15.

8 ■ ■ ■ ■ 38

16.

$-\frac{2}{4}$ ■ ■ ■ $\frac{2}{4}$

17.

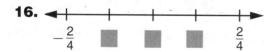

3.4 ■ ■ ■ ■ ■ 4.6

18.

19 ■ ■ 61

Write all of your answers on a separate sheet of paper.

Add or subtract.

19. $\frac{3}{10} + \frac{3}{10}$

20. $\frac{11}{12} - \frac{1}{2}$

21. $\frac{7}{8} - \frac{2}{8}$

22. $\frac{3}{4} + \frac{1}{12}$

23. $\frac{1}{4} + \frac{3}{4}$

24. $\frac{5}{6} - \frac{1}{4}$

Round 53,729,437 to the nearest

25. hundred

26. thousand

27. hundred-thousand

28. million

Solve.

29. $60 * n = 3,600$

30. $s * 7 = 49$

31. $g * 32 = 640$

32. $2 * m = 960$

33. $b * 7 = 350$

34. $j * 90 = 360$

35. $8 * f = 640$

36. $6 * a = 72$

Use the clues to find the number.

37. Clue 1: I am a prime number less than 75.
Clue 2: My digits sum to 13.

38. Clue 1: I am an even number.
Clue 2: I am less than 65, but greater than 50.
Clue 3: I am divisible by 5.

Practice Set 48

Write all of your answers on a separate sheet of paper.

Solve.

1. $-15 + 2$

2. $-4 + -5$

3. $62 + -9$

4. $-8 + -1$

5. $-14 + 6$

6. $250 + -110$

7. $-61 + 60$

8. $-90 + -30$

9. $-43 + 43$

10. $29 + -15$

Use digits to write the following numbers.

11. one hundred twenty-two billion, three hundred twelve million, eighty-five thousand

12. eighty-four and sixteen hundredths

13. eighteen trillion, two hundred thousand, fourteen

Write the following numbers in words.

14. 83,900,000,000,001

15. 14.657

16. 4,296,087,050,000

Solve.

17. $18 + b = 142$

18. $900 \div c = 30$

19. $12 + t = 50$

20. $n * 10 = 650$

21. $a \div 5 = 70$

22. $16.75 - h = 12$

Use with or after Lesson 7.7.

Write all of your answers on a separate sheet of paper.

Use the thermometer number line to help you solve the subtraction problems.

Example On Monday the temperature was 8°F. By Tuesday the temperature had dropped 15°F. What was the temperature on Tuesday?

8   Start at 8°F.

− 15   Go down 15°F.

−7   The result is −7°F, or 7° below zero Fahrenheit.

1. 80°F − 40°F = ■

2. 40°F − 60°F = ■

3. 6°F − 9°F = ■

4. 12°F − 18°F = ■

5. ■ = 80°F − 120°F

6. ■ = 60°F − 35°F

7. 8°F − 82°F = ■

8. 45°F − 39°F = ■

9. ■ = 6°F − 11°F

10. 29°F − 48°F = ■

11. 3°F − 25°F = ■

12. 32°F − 64°F = ■

13. −18°F − 55°F = ■

14. −90°F + 30°F = ■

100° —— 100°
90° —— 90°
80° —— 80°
70° —— 70°
60° —— 60°
50° —— 50°
40° —— 40°
30° —— 30°
20° —— 20°
10° —— 10°
5° —— 5°
0° —— 0°
−5° —— −5°
−10° —— −10°
−20° —— −20°
−30° —— −30°
−40° —— −40°
−50° —— −50°
−60° —— −60°

Write all of your answers on a separate sheet of paper.

Write the next three numbers in the pattern.

15. 0.555, 0.535, 0.515

16. 4.2, 3.2, 2.2

17. 1, $\frac{1}{10}$, $\frac{1}{100}$

18. −65, −85, −105

Write the amounts.

19. 2(Q), 4(D), 4(N), 1(P)

20. 4 $1 , 1(Q), 2(D), 1(N), 2(P)

21. 3 $5 , 1 $1 , 2(Q), 1(N)

22. 1 $100 , 4 $20 , 1 $5 , 1 $1 , 1(Q), 14(N), 17(P)

> 1 km = 1000 m
> 1 m = 100 cm
> 1 cm = 10 mm

If 1 centimeter on a map represents 500 kilometers, then find the following:

23. 7 cm represents ■ km.

24. 280 mm represents ■ km.

25. 63 cm represents ■ km.

26. 9.5 cm represents ■ km.

27. 65 mm represents ■ km.

Write all of your answers on a separate sheet of paper.

Find the account balance.

1.

2.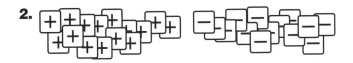

3.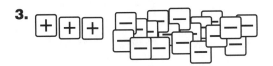

4.

5.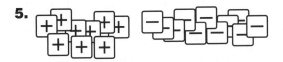

6.

Write all of your answers on a separate sheet of paper.

Complete.

7. $100^2 = \blacksquare$

8. $6^{\blacksquare} = 216$

9. $11 * 11 * 11 = 11^{\blacksquare}$

10. The square root of $676 = \blacksquare$

Solve.

11. $\frac{2}{8}$
$-\frac{1}{16}$

12. 48
$* 13$

13. 28
$* 39$

14. $79,430$
$- 31,451$

15. 43
$* 92$

16. $\frac{6}{14}$
$-\frac{3}{4}$

17. 439
$+ 100$

18. $136,343$
$* 5$

---

19. Write the missing numbers for the table.

Fraction	Percent	Decimal
$\frac{1}{5}$	$\blacksquare$	$\blacksquare$
$\blacksquare$	$\blacksquare$	0.57
$\blacksquare$	75%	$\blacksquare$
$\blacksquare$	81%	$\blacksquare$
$\blacksquare$	$\blacksquare$	0.99

Use with or after Lesson 7.10.

Write all of your answers on a separate sheet of paper.

Compare. Write >, <, or =.

1. $\frac{3}{5}$ ■ $\frac{10}{15}$

2. $\frac{3}{4}$ ■ $\frac{8}{12}$

3. $\frac{3}{10}$ ■ $\frac{2}{5}$

4. $\frac{3}{6}$ ■ $\frac{3}{7}$

5. $\frac{3}{9}$ ■ $\frac{1}{3}$

6. $\frac{5}{8}$ ■ $\frac{9}{16}$

7. $\frac{12}{20}$ ■ $\frac{2}{5}$

8. $\frac{7}{8}$ ■ $\frac{11}{12}$

Mr. Edwards records points for homework assignments. Each student in the class is represented in the stem-and-leaf plot.

9. How many students are in the class?

10. What is the maximum?

11. What is the minimum?

12. What is the mode?

13. What is the median?

14. What is the mean?

Homework Points

Stems (10s)	Leaves (1s)
4	1 3 3 5 7
5	0 4 5 6 6 6
6	2 5 7 9 9
7	2 5 7 7
8	0

Practice Set 52

Write all of your answers on a separate sheet of paper.

Rename each as a whole number or a mixed number in simplest form.

1. $\frac{12}{8}$ **2.** $\frac{6}{3}$ **3.** $\frac{27}{8}$

4. $\frac{16}{5}$ **5.** $\frac{36}{4}$ **6.** $\frac{19}{6}$

Add. Write each sum as a whole number or mixed number in simplest form.

7. $3\frac{1}{2} + 2\frac{1}{2}$ **8.** $4\frac{1}{8} + 2\frac{3}{8}$

9. $6\frac{1}{3} + 8\frac{2}{3}$ **10.** $1\frac{4}{5} + 3\frac{3}{5}$

11. $7\frac{2}{9} + 3\frac{8}{9}$ **12.** $2\frac{3}{10} + 4\frac{1}{5}$

13. $3\frac{1}{6} + 4\frac{5}{12}$ **14.** $4\frac{1}{12} + 1\frac{1}{3}$

Tell whether each number sentence is *true* or *false*.

15. $20 + (10 * 7.4) = 94$ **16.** $70 = (11 * 5) + 18$

17. $32 + (18 * 6) = 132$ **18.** $35 - (99 / 9) = 24$

Put these numbers in order from smallest to largest.

19. 4.8   0.84   4.008   4,000.08   80,000.4

20. 20.1   2.01   0.21   201.2   120.1

Write all of your answers on a separate sheet of paper.

> The three angles of a triangle always add up
> to 180°. A right angle measures 90°.

21. What is the measure of angle *T*?

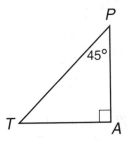

22. What is the measure of angle *R*?

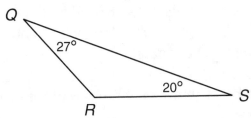

Fill in the missing numbers on the number lines.

23.

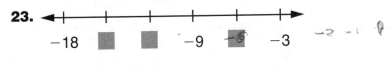

−18 ▢ ▢ −9 ▢ −3

24.

106 ▢ ▢ ▢ ▢ 656

Write all of your answers on a separate sheet of paper.

Subtract. Write your answers in simplest form.

1. $5 - \frac{5}{6}$

2. $9 - \frac{5}{12}$

3. $6 - 1\frac{1}{4}$

4. $10 - 8\frac{2}{3}$

5. $3\frac{3}{4} - 2\frac{1}{4}$

6. $9\frac{5}{6} - 7\frac{1}{6}$

7. $9\frac{1}{5} - 4\frac{2}{5}$

8. $7\frac{11}{12} - 2\frac{5}{12}$

Solve.

9. $(15 - 15) * 4$

10. $65 - (6 * 9)$

11. $(560 + 70) / 30$

12. $(900 / 3) + 40$

13. The temperature at noon was 18°F. With the wind chill it was −4°F. How much colder is the wind chill than the normal temperature?

Rewrite the number sentences with parentheses to make them correct.

14. $880 = 80 * 16 + 2 - 7$

15. $7 * 12 - 6 = 42$

16. $144 = 8 + 4 * 12$

17. $37 - 18 - 5 = 24$

18. $45 - 18 + 31 = -4$

19. $56 = 8 + 4 * 12$

20. $45 - 18 + 31 = 58$

21. $5 * 8 + 6 * 9 = 94$

Write all of your answers on a separate sheet of paper.

Solve.

22. You start with a number. Double it. Square the answer. You get 400. What number did you start with?

23. You start with a number. Double it. Square the answer. You get 1,296. What number did you start with?

Write >, <, or = to make each sentence true.

24. $\frac{1}{4} + \frac{1}{2}$ ■ $\frac{4}{6}$

25. $2\frac{4}{12}$ ■ 2.5

26. $\frac{12}{2}$ ■ $80 / 10$

27. 12.5 ■ $25 / 2$

28. $\frac{3}{5}$ ■ $\frac{4}{10}$

29. $3\frac{3}{8}$ ■ $\frac{25}{8}$

Complete the "What's My Rule?" tables.

30.

Rule	in	out
out = in / 3	4,260	1,420
	2,100	
	6,399	
	4,584	
		85

31.

Rule	in	out
out = in * 3.5	27	
	33	
		14
	24	
	51	

Write all of your answers on a separate sheet of paper.

Write the letter of the picture that best represents each expression.

1. $\frac{1}{4}$ of $\frac{1}{2}$

A.

2. $\frac{2}{3}$ of $\frac{1}{4}$

B.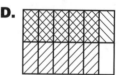

3. $\frac{1}{2}$ of $\frac{5}{6}$

C.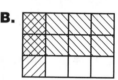

4. $\frac{3}{4}$ of $\frac{1}{6}$

D.

---

5. What is the name of the polygon?

6. If each side were 6.5 inches, what would the perimeter of the figure be?

7. How many lines of symmetry does it have?

Write all of your answers on a separate sheet of paper.

Find the product. Use area models to help you.

1. $5 * \frac{2}{3}$

2. $\frac{1}{5} * 6$

3. $4 * \frac{1}{4}$

4. $7 * \frac{1}{3}$

5. $\frac{3}{5} * 6$

6. $4 * \frac{3}{8}$

Compare. Write < or >.

7. -3.8 ■ -2

8. -1.03 ■ -1.3

9. 0.5 ■ -1.5

10. 23 ■ -25

11. -45 ■ -52

12. -1.0 ■ -0.1

Write a number sentence, then solve. Tell what you did about the remainder.

13. Mari sells eggs by the dozen. One week her chickens laid 152 eggs. How many dozen eggs did she have to sell that week?

14. There are 137 fifth graders going on a field trip to the museum. The school buses each hold 62 students. How many buses are needed for the trip?

15. Sheri weighs a bag of tomatoes. It weighs 40 ounces. How many pounds of tomatoes are in the bag?

Write all of your answers on a separate sheet of paper.

Use digits to write the following numbers.

16. two hundred sixty million, eighty-four thousand, four hundred fifty-three

17. six hundred eighty-six and thirty-eight hundredths

18. three billion, four hundred fourteen million, six hundred ninety-one thousand

19. nine hundred sixty-eight and eleven thousandths

20. six trillion, seventy-two billion, eighteen

Write the words for the following numbers.

21. 2,000,000,002

22. 312,743,000

23. 54.098

24. 4,969,231,238

25. 32.906

26. 6,742,843

27. 0.505

28. 43.003

Complete the "What's My Rule?" tables.

29.

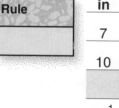

Rule	in	out
	7	$15\frac{1}{4}$
	10	$18\frac{1}{4}$
		20
	$13\frac{1}{2}$	
	$22\frac{3}{4}$	31

30.

Rule: out = in * 7	in	out
	4	
		35
		70
	6	
	8	

Write all of your answers on a separate sheet of paper.

Multiply. Write your answer in simplest form.

1. $3\frac{1}{3} * \frac{4}{5}$

2. $\frac{1}{2} * \frac{5}{8}$

3. $7 * 2\frac{1}{3}$

4. $4\frac{1}{6} * 2\frac{2}{5}$

5. $3\frac{1}{8} * 6\frac{3}{5}$

6. $3\frac{1}{3} * \frac{3}{10}$

Complete the following number lines.

7. 500 ▨ ▨ ▨ ▨ ▨ 6,500

8. 15 ▨ ▨ ▨ 355

9. 2 ▨ ▨ ▨ ▨ 82

Round each number to the nearest hundredth.

10. 18.985

11. 5.264

12. 344.745

13. 23.536

14. 29.904

15. 0.026

16. 461.066

17. 0.178

18. 82.721

19. 7.921

20. 94.387

21. 102.431

22. 521.767

23. 187.889

Write all of your answers on a separate sheet of paper.

Write a decimal and a percent for each fraction.

1. $\frac{73}{100}$ **2.** $\frac{1}{2}$ **3.** $\frac{3}{4}$

4. $\frac{45}{100}$ **5.** $\frac{1}{3}$ **6.** $\frac{3}{5}$

7. $\frac{9}{10}$ **8.** $\frac{8}{50}$ **9.** $\frac{3}{20}$

Maury bought a new shirt that was on sale at 15% off the original price. The original price was $30.

10. How much will he pay?

11. How much money will Maury save on the shirt?

Measure to the nearest $\frac{1}{2}$ cm.

12. •———•

13. •————————————•

Solve.

14.   12
    $* 9$

15.   52
    $- 38$

16.   258
    $+ 3,217$

17. 6,323
    $- 236$

18.   10
    $* 8$

19.   75
    $- 22$

20.   876
    $+ 921$

21. 8,614
    $+ 125$

22. $1\frac{2}{3}$
    $-1\frac{1}{3}$

23. $7\frac{5}{8}$
    $+1\frac{1}{8}$

24. $9\frac{7}{10}$
    $+3\frac{3}{10}$

25. $6\frac{2}{5}$
    $+4\frac{2}{5}$

     Use with or after Lesson 8.9.

Write all of your answers on a separate sheet of paper.

Sally, John, and Jeff drove from Denver to Chicago. Sally drove $\frac{2}{9}$ of the distance. John drove $\frac{1}{3}$ of the distance. Jeff drove the rest of the way.

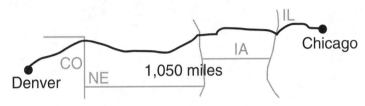

26. How many miles did Sally drive?

27. How many miles did John drive?

28. How many miles did Jeff drive?

Write >, <, or = to make each sentence true.

29. $\frac{1}{4}$ ■ $\frac{3}{6}$

30. $1\frac{4}{12}$ ■ $\frac{5}{3}$

31. $\frac{8}{2}$ ■ $\frac{9}{10}$

32. 4.5 ■ 25 / 5

33. $\frac{1}{5}$ ■ $\frac{2}{10}$

Complete the "What's My Rule?" tables.

34.

Rule: out = in × 710	in	out
	6	4,260
	8	
	9	
	11	
	15	

35.

Rule: out = in / 3	in	out
	27	
	33	
		14
	24	
	51	

Write all of your answers on a separate sheet of paper.

Solve.

1. $\frac{1}{10}$ of 90   **2.** $\frac{2}{5}$ of 250

3. $\frac{3}{8}$ of 24   **4.** $\frac{1}{40}$ of 160

5. $\frac{9}{16}$ of 32   **6.** $\frac{2}{4}$ of 90

7. $\frac{9}{8}$ of 64   **8.** $\frac{9}{9}$ of 81

9. $\frac{7}{8}$ of 16   **10.** $\frac{6}{8}$ of 72

11. $\frac{4}{3}$ of 18   **12.** $\frac{5}{6}$ of 30

---

13. Use the clues to write a seven-digit number.
- Multiply 9 by 12. Subtract 100. Write the result in the hundreds place.
- Triple the number in the hundreds place and then divide by 4. Write the result in the millions place.
- Divide 3,300 by 1,100. Add 1 and write the result in the hundred-thousands place.
- Double the number in the millions place and divide by 6. Write the result in the tens place.
- Add 3 to the number in the tens place. Write the result in the ten-thousands place.
- Find 2% of 50. Write the result in the ones place.
- Divide 630 by 90. Write the result in the thousands place.

Write all of your answers on a separate sheet of paper.

14. Copy and then complete the Powers of 10 Table.

The Powers of 10 Table

Millions	Hundred-Thousands	Ten-Thousands	Thousands	Hundreds	Tens	Ones
	100,000			100		1
	10 [10,000s]			10 [10s]		10 [0.1s]
			10*10*10			
10^6			10^3			10^0

Write all of your answers on a separate sheet of paper.

Solve.

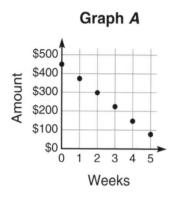

Graph A

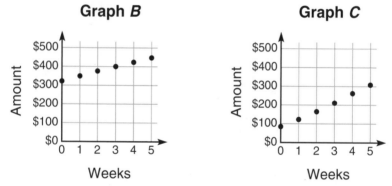

Graph B

Graph C

1. Susan deposited $45 every week during a five-week period. After three weeks, she had a little more than $200. Which graph depicts her account value?

2. Tom withdrew $75 every week for five weeks. Which graph depicts his account value?

3. After five weeks of regular deposits, Julian's account balance was $450. Which graph depicts his account value?

4. If Julian continued making regular weekly deposits, how long would it take him to save $1,000?

Write all of your answers on a separate sheet of paper.

Solve.

5.   300
      − 600

6.   62,473
      + 5,268

7.   253
      + 253

8. 2,352
     − 967

9. $26 - (-7)$

10.   35
       − 63

11.   264
       + 656

12.   12,965
       − 1,583

13.   4,322
       − 3,362

14. How much is $\frac{5}{8}$ of 32¢?

15. How much is $\frac{2}{12}$ of 54¢?

16. How much is $\frac{1}{10}$ of $8.30?

17. How much is $\frac{1}{3}$ of $3.60?

18. How much is $\frac{2}{5}$ of $2.20?

19. How much is $\frac{6}{3}$ of 27¢?

Complete.

20. $3^4 = \blacksquare$

21. $5^\blacksquare = 3,125$

22. $6 * 6 * 6 * 6 = \blacksquare$ **23.** 10 to the fourth power $= \blacksquare$

Rewrite the number sentences with parentheses to make them correct.

24. $43 - 24 - 8 = 27$

25. $19 - 35 - 8 = -8$

26. $6 * 9 + 3 * 14 = 1,008$ **27.** $240 = 10 * 6 + 18$

28. $370 = 5 * 9 + 65$

29. $398 = 8 * 43 + 68 - 14$

30. $10 * 10 - 5^2 = 75$

31. $7 * 6^2 - 4^2 = 140$

Write all of your answers on a separate sheet of paper.

Write the number pairs for each point.

1. *A*   **2.** *C*

3. *E*   **4.** *G*

Name the point at each number pair.

5. (0, 4)   **6.** (−4, 4)

7. (4, −4)   **8.** (2, −4)

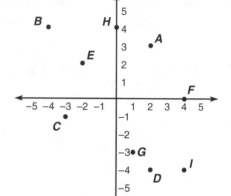

What are the next three numbers in each pattern?

9. 40, 80, 160   **10.** 9, 18, 36

11. $\frac{6}{4}, \frac{12}{4}, \frac{24}{4}$ **12.** $\frac{1}{8}, \frac{3}{8}, \frac{5}{8}$

Write the amounts.

13. (Q)(Q)(Q)(D)(D)(N)(N)(P)(P)(P)

14. $1 (Q)(Q)(Q)(D)(D)(N)(N)(N)(P)(P)

15. $1 | $1 | $1 | $1 | $1 | $1 | $1
(Q)(N)

Write all of your answers on a separate sheet of paper.

Find the area.

1.

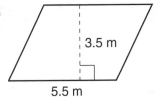

3.5 m

5.5 m

2.

4 ft

12 ft

3.

2.6 km

3.8 km

Use the following list of numbers to answer the questions.

18.5, 16.25, 15.75, 13.5, 19.25, 11.5, 22.5, 14.25, 11.5

4. What is the range?   **5.** What is the mode?

6. What is the median?   **7.** What is the mean?

Write all of your answers on a separate sheet of paper.

Solve.

8. 375
    * 24

9.   65.9
    + 93.6

10. 41.70
    + 2.57

11.   3.88
    − 2.92

12. 12
    * 18

13. 63
    − 73

14. $\dfrac{2}{3}$
    + $\dfrac{4}{3}$

15. $\dfrac{14}{8}$
    − $\dfrac{1}{16}$

16. 634
    + 274

17. 3,435
    + 285

18. 28
    * 9

19. 378
    * 5

Complete the "What's My Rule?" tables.

20.

Rule: out = in + $\frac{1}{4}$	in	out
	$\frac{1}{4}$	
	$\frac{1}{2}$	
	$\frac{3}{4}$	
	$\frac{2}{8}$	
	$\frac{5}{8}$	

21.

Rule: out = in − 1.1	in	out
	2.7	
	3.3	
		1.4
	2.4	
	8	6.9

Complete.

22. 84 days = ■ weeks

23. 2.5 hours = ■ seconds

24. 10% of a day = ■ minutes

Write all of your answers on a separate sheet of paper.

Find the volume of each prism.

| Volume = length * width * height |
| Volume = Base * height |

1.

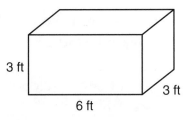

3 ft

3 ft

6 ft

2.

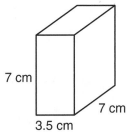

7 cm

7 cm

3.5 cm

3.

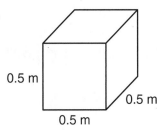

0.5 m

0.5 m

0.5 m

4.

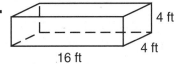

4 ft

4 ft

16 ft

5.

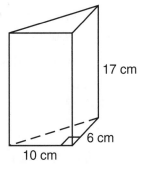

17 cm

6 cm

10 cm

6.

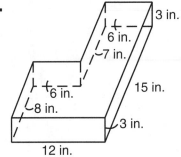

3 in.

6 in.

7 in.

6 in.

8 in.

15 in.

3 in.

12 in.

Write all of your answers on a separate sheet of paper.

What are the next three numbers in each pattern?

7. −15, −10, −5

8. 0.04, 0.06, 0.08

9. 0.44, 0.68, 0.92

Use the information in the table to answer the questions below. Round to the nearest whole number.

Year	U.S. Population	Number of Children Ages 5 to 14
1900	76,000,000	17,000,000
1990	255,000,000	28,000,000

10. In 1900, about what percent of the population was 5 to 14 years old?

11. About what percent of the population was 5 to 14 years old in 1990?

12. About how many times larger was the entire U.S. population in 1990 than in 1900?

13. About how many times larger was the population of 5- to 14-year olds?

14. Did the ratio of children to the U.S. population increase or decrease from 1900 to 1990?

15. Why do you think the ratio changed?

16. 76,000,000 can be written using scientific notation as 7.6×10^7. Write all other numbers in the table using scientific notation.

Practice Set 63

Write all of your answers on a separate sheet of paper.

Complete.

1. 3 L = _____ mL
2. 150 cm^3 = _____ mL
3. 0.5 L = _____ mL
4. 4,200 cm^3 = _____ L
5. 1 gallon = _____ quarts
6. 3 quarts = _____ pints
7. 96 ounces = _____ quarts
8. 3 cups = _____ ounces

9. Find the area of each rectangle below. Write a number model to represent each.

Example: Rectangle $A = 2 * 5 = 10$ square units.

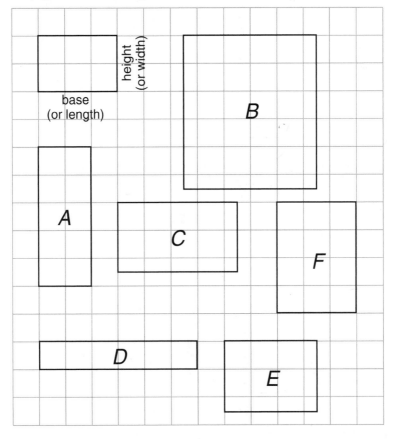

Write all of your answers on a separate sheet of paper.

Solve the pan-balance problems.

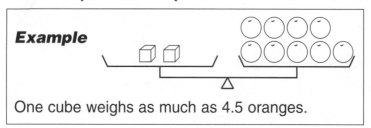

Example

One cube weighs as much as 4.5 oranges.

1.

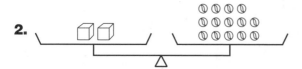

One orange weighs as much as ■ grapes.

2.

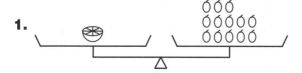

One block weighs as much as ■ marbles.

3.

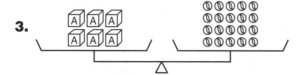

One block weighs as much as ■ marbles.

4.

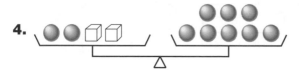

One cube weighs as much as ■ balls.

Use with or after Lesson 10.2.

Write all of your answers on a separate sheet of paper.

Solve.

5. 2.5 * 4.3

6. 1.2 * 0.35

7. 41.7 * 0.8

8. 58.285 + 18.572

9. 845.9 + 38.2

10. 582.967 + 93.837

11. 306.403 – 217.284

12. 572.25 – 23.41

13. For relay races, the gym teacher divided the class into 5 teams with an equal number of students on each team. Extra students helped judge the race. There were 28 students. How many judges were there?

14. Mrs. Krupa made 146 ounces of stewed tomatoes. How many 6-ounce jars can she fill?

Simplify the fractions.

15. $1\frac{8}{20}$ **16.** $4\frac{8}{12}$ **17.** $\frac{54}{6}$ **18.** $8\frac{12}{48}$ **19.** $\frac{26}{12}$ **20.** $\frac{19}{4}$

21. $\frac{90}{15}$ **22.** $\frac{22}{11}$ **23.** $\frac{15}{45}$ **24.** $\frac{27}{81}$ **25.** $\frac{42}{77}$ **26.** $\frac{16}{56}$

Write number sentences for the following; then tell whether each is *true* or *false*.

27. If 8.5 is subtracted from 24.6, the result is 16.1.

28. 11 is twice as much as 5.5.

29. 275 is more than $700 * \frac{3}{4}$.

30. Divide 68 by 2 and you get 34.

31. If 58 is decreased by 16, the result is −48.

32. 45 is greater than the sum of 76 and (−35).

Write all of your answers on a separate sheet of paper.

Complete the "What's My Rule?" tables.

1.

Rule	in	out
out = in * 14	3	
	5	
	7	
	11	
	15	

2.

Rule	in	out
out = in / 15	30	
	105	
	705	
	1,170	
	1,530	

3.

Rule	in	out
out = in − 75	60	
	123	
		35
	11	
		−82

4.

Rule	in	out
	8	18.25
	14	24.25
		44.75
	35	
	48.75	59

Find the following landmarks for the set of numbers:

27, 18, 46, 33, 30, 27, 14, 25

5. maximum   **6.** minimum   **7.** range
8. median   **9.** mean   **10.** mode

Compare. Write <, >, or = .

11. −3.05 ■ −3.15   **12.** −127 ■ −172
13. $\frac{10}{12}$ ■ $\frac{5}{6}$ **14.** $1\frac{1}{5}$ ■ $\frac{7}{5}$
15. −1.5 ■ −1$\frac{1}{2}$ **16.** −0.42 ■ −$\frac{6}{10}$

Write all of your answers on a separate sheet of paper.

Write the x- and y-coordinates for each point.

1. A **2.** B

3. C **4.** D

5. E **6.** F

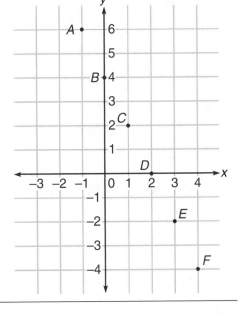

Solve.

7. $\frac{1}{4}$ of 80

8. $\frac{1}{6}$ of 240

9. $\frac{4}{5}$ of 25

10. $\frac{1}{40}$ of 1,200

11. $\frac{1}{16}$ of 32

12. $\frac{20}{30}$ of 90

13. $\frac{5}{8}$ of 64

14. $\frac{7}{9}$ of 81

15. Lucky Video is going out of business. All videos are $\frac{1}{3}$ the regular price. Sal's Videos has a 50%-off sale. Which store has a better sale?

16. If a video originally cost $15, how much will it be at Lucky Video?

Write all of your answers on a separate sheet of paper.

Write the algebraic expression that best matches each situation.

17. Ellen jogs 3 miles each day. How many miles does she jog in *d* days?

$3 * d$ $\qquad$ $3 + d$ $\qquad$ $d \div 3$

18. Tim takes $17 from his savings account. How much is left in his savings account?

$s - 17$ $\qquad$ $s + 17$ $\qquad$ $17 * s$

19. Mr. Gomez drove *m* miles in 8 hours. How many miles did he drive per hour?

$m * 8$ $\qquad$ $m / 8$ $\qquad$ $m + 8$

Solve. Write the answer in simplest form.

20. $3\frac{1}{2} + 2\frac{1}{5}$

21. $9 - 5\frac{1}{8}$

22. $4\frac{1}{4} + 6\frac{1}{6}$

23. $8\frac{1}{3} * \frac{1}{2}$

24. $9\frac{1}{2} - 7\frac{2}{3}$

25. $4\frac{1}{3} * 2\frac{2}{5}$

Round 4,871,354 to the nearest

26. million

27. ten-thousand

28. hundred-thousand

29. hundred

Write all of your answers on a separate sheet of paper.

Match each of the events with one of the graphs.

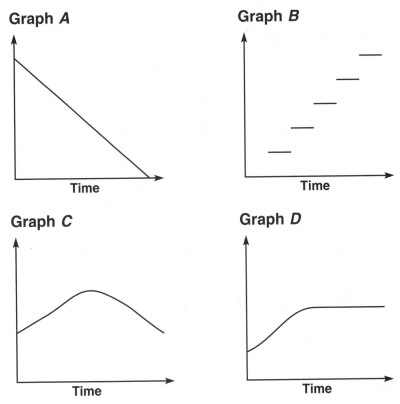

Graph A

Time

Graph B

Time

Graph C

Time

Graph D

Time

1. The temperature outside on the patio during the day from sunrise to sunset.

2. The amount of money in Fred's savings account. He makes a deposit at the end of each week.

3. The volume of water in a sink as the water drains out.

4. The temperature of a pan of water that heats on the stove to boiling.

Write all of your answers on a separate sheet of paper.

Write the following numbers in digits.

5. eighteen trillion, six hundred twenty-seven billion, nine hundred million

6. nine billion, one hundred fifty-six million

7. six hundred fourteen trillion, four hundred million

Write the following numbers in words.

8. 218,055,000   **9.** 168,409,000

10. 34,313,000,000   **11.** 1,867,291,433

Solve.

12. $65\overline{)910}$ **13.** $35\overline{)1,680}$ **14.** $\begin{array}{r} 7,940 \\ +\ 56,094 \end{array}$ **15.** $\begin{array}{r} 6,521 \\ -\ 3,876 \end{array}$

16. $\begin{array}{r} \frac{3}{4} \\ -\ \frac{1}{4} \end{array}$ **17.** $\begin{array}{r} 7,547 \\ +\ 4,546 \end{array}$ **18.** $\begin{array}{r} 645 \\ +\ 64,900 \end{array}$ **19.** $\begin{array}{r} 364.0 \\ -\ 4.5 \end{array}$

20. $\begin{array}{r} 3.970 \\ -\ 1.050 \end{array}$ **21.** $\begin{array}{r} 18.2 \\ *\ 4 \end{array}$ **22.** $\begin{array}{r} 363 \\ -\ 34 \end{array}$ **23.** $\begin{array}{r} 98 \\ -\ 63 \end{array}$

24. $\frac{1}{2} * 68$ **25.** $8\overline{)328}$ **26.** $\begin{array}{r} 470 \\ *\ 30 \end{array}$ **27.** $\begin{array}{r} 3,643 \\ +\ 534 \end{array}$

Complete.

28. $10^4 = \blacksquare$ **29.** $6^{\blacksquare} = 1,296$

30. $16^2 = \blacksquare$ **31.** $9^{\blacksquare} = 729$

Use with or after Lesson 10.7.

Write all of your answers on a separate sheet of paper.

Find the area of each figure below.

1.

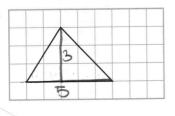

2.

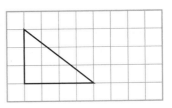

3.

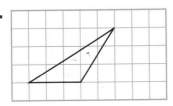

4.

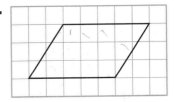

5.

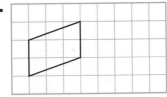

6.

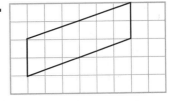

Tell whether each number is prime or composite.

7. 51   **8.** 323   **9.** 119

10. 101   **11.** 99   **12.** 67

13. 2   **14.** 143   **15.** 891

Write all of your answers on a separate sheet of paper.

> Diameter = 2 * Radius
> Circumference = π * Diameter

1. Find the circumference.

5.7 cm

2. What is the radius of the tire?

68"

Find the area of each circle.

3.

7"

4.

18 cm

Tell which measurement would be best for each situation. Write *area, circumference,* or *perimeter.*

5. The amount of fence needed to enclose a rectangular garden.

6. The amount of fabric needed to cover the top of a round table.

7. The amount of lace needed to trim the outside edge of a circular table cloth.

8. The amount of carpet needed to cover a rectangular floor.

Write all of your answers on a separate sheet of paper.

Complete each rate table below. Then answer the questions.

> **Example** Susan's car gets about 35 miles per gallon of gasoline on the highway.
>
> | miles | 35 | 70 | 105 | 140 | 175 | 210 |
> |---|---|---|---|---|---|---|
> | gallons | 1 | 2 | 3 | 4 | 5 | 6 |

9. How far can the car travel on 6 gallons of gas?

10. At 140 miles, how many gallons have been used?

The cows on the McCulhay farm each produce about 8 gallons of milk per day.

gallons	8	■	■	■	■	■	■
cows	1	10	50	100	250	500	7

11. If 250 cows are milked every day, how many gallons of milk will be produced in a week?

12. If 250 cows are milked for 30 days and 500 cows for 20 days, how many gallons of milk will be produced?

Find the unit rate for each. Then tell which is the better buy.

13. 1 dozen eggs for $2.64
1 half-dozen eggs for $1.50

14. 3 cans of tomato sauce for $1.05
2 cans of tomato sauce for $0.89

15. 3 pounds of apples for $2.88
40 pounds of apples for $26.00

Write all of your answers on a separate sheet of paper.

Identify each figure. Write *prism, pyramid, cylinder, cone,* or *sphere.*

1.

2.

3.

4.

5.

6.

Rewrite each pair of fractions, using the least common denominator. Then compare the fractions. Write >, <, or =.

7. $\frac{1}{2}$ ■ $\frac{6}{7}$

8. $\frac{2}{3}$ ■ $\frac{8}{15}$

9. $\frac{11}{20}$ ■ $\frac{1}{12}$

10. $\frac{4}{9}$ ■ $\frac{7}{10}$

11. $\frac{5}{8}$ ■ $\frac{3}{5}$

12. $\frac{3}{21}$ ■ $\frac{2}{15}$

Use with or after Lesson 11.1.

Write all of your answers on a separate sheet of paper.

Match each shape with at least one property. More than 1 property may apply.

1. triangular prism

2. tetrahedron

3. cube

4. cone

5. cylinder

A. At least 1 surface is a circle.

B. All surfaces are triangles.

C. All surfaces are the same shape.

D. The faces are rectangles, but not the bases.

E. There is only 1 base.

6. Write the missing numbers for the table.

Product	Exponential Notation	Standard Notation
8 * 8 * 8	■	■
■	10^5	■
■	$2^■$	32
12 * 12 * 12	■	■
■	■	256

Complete the missing factors.

7. ■ * 70 = 350

8. 30 * ■ = 810

9. ■ * 11 = 6,600

10. 80 * ■ = 560

11. ■ * 9 = 360

12. ■ * 32 = 640

13. 11 * ■ = 770

14. 140 * ■ = 280

Write all of your answers on a separate sheet of paper.

Rename the following fractions as decimals.

15. $\frac{6}{10}$ **16.** $\frac{3}{4}$ **17.** $\frac{8}{24}$

18. $\frac{16}{10}$ **19.** $\frac{769}{1,000}$ **20.** $\frac{28}{100}$

21. $\frac{7}{8}$ **22.** $2\frac{3}{4}$ **23.** $\frac{18}{16}$

24. $\frac{734}{100}$ **25.** $5\frac{321}{1,000}$ **26.** $\frac{180}{18}$

Find the missing angle measurements without using a protractor.

27. $x = \blacksquare^\circ$

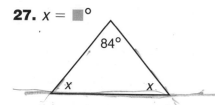

When two lines bisect, they form opposite angles of equal measure.

28. $a = \blacksquare^\circ$ **29.** $b = \blacksquare^\circ$

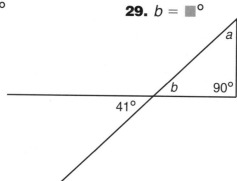

Write all of your answers on a separate sheet of paper.

Find the volume of each figure.

$$V = B * h$$

1.

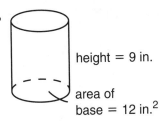

height = 9 in.

area of
base = 12 in.²

2.

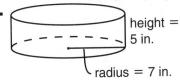

height =
5 in.

radius = 7 in.

3.

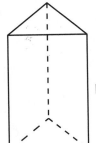

height = 12 in.

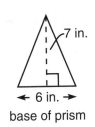

7 in.

← 6 in. →

base of prism

Solve.

4. 523
  * 20

5. 353
  − 75

6. 25
  − 7

7.   250
  + 2,700

8.   235
  + 2,352

9. 35)3,115

10. 542
  * 21

11. 26)1,066

12.   7,345
  − 3,462

Write all of your answers on a separate sheet of paper.

Complete the "What's My Rule?" tables.

13.

Rule	in	out
out = in × 300	9	
	12	
	15	
	25	
	100	

14.

Rule	in	out
	7	17.5
	10	25
		12.5
	18	
	100	250

15.

Rule	in	out
out = in − 55	80	
	160	
		90
	2,400	
		1,200

16.

Rule	in	out
	800	20
	160	
		90
	2,400	
	4,800	120

Tamara wants to save $80 during her summer vacation. After 2 weeks she has saved $16.

17. What fraction of the $80 did she save in the first 2 weeks?

18. What percent did she save?

19. At this rate, how long will it take her to save $80?

Use with or after Lesson 11.3.

Write all of your answers on a separate sheet of paper.

Find the volume of each figure.

> Prism and Cylinder $V = B * h$
> Pyramid and Cone $V = \frac{1}{3} * (B * h)$

1.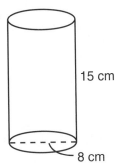

15 cm

8 cm

2.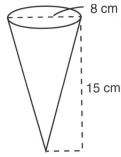

8 cm

15 cm

3.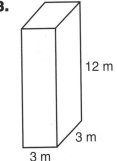

12 m

3 m

3 m

4.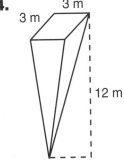

3 m

3 m

12 m

Write each fraction as a mixed number or a whole number.

5. $\frac{30}{12}$ **6.** $\frac{24}{8}$ **7.** $\frac{9}{4}$

8. $\frac{50}{15}$ **9.** $\frac{85}{20}$ **10.** $\frac{66}{9}$

Solve.

11. $-20 - (-56)$ **12.** $-4 + (-24)$

13. $17 + (-20)$ **14.** $-3 - 42$

Use with or after Lesson 11.4.

Write all of your answers on a separate sheet of paper.

Complete. You may use a calculator.

15. $8^3 = \blacksquare$ **16.** $7^4 = \blacksquare$

17. $3^6 = \blacksquare$ **18.** $4^5 = \blacksquare$

19. $6^7 = \blacksquare$ **20.** $\blacksquare^3 = 125$

21. $8^{\blacksquare} = 32{,}768$ **22.** $\blacksquare^6 = 64$

Find the total cost.

23. 7 rulers that cost 45¢ each

24. 9 scissors that cost $2.65 each

25. 28 books that cost $1.15 each

Solve.

26.   9,376
        $+ 4{,}329$

27.   1,754
        $+ 2{,}845$

28. 1,000
        $- 43$

29. 20,000
        $* 5$

30. $300 * \frac{1}{3}$

31. $\begin{aligned} 5\frac{1}{4} \\ + 3\frac{1}{2} \end{aligned}$

32. 532
        $- 58$

33. 234
        $- 18$

34. 234
        $* 52$

35. 721
        $* 82$

36. 687
        $* 25$

37. $\begin{aligned} 9\frac{3}{4} \\ + 10\frac{1}{4} \end{aligned}$

Write all of your answers on a separate sheet of paper.

Complete.

1. 2 pints = _____ quart(s)

2. 8 ounces = _____ cup(s)

3. 18 quarts = _____ cup(s)

4. 1 gallon = _____ pint(s)

5. 3 half-gallons = _____ ounce(s)

6. 7 pints = _____ quart(s)

7. 100 ounces = _____ cup(s)

8. 4 pints = _____ cup(s)

Measure each angle to the nearest degree.

9. 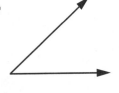   **10.**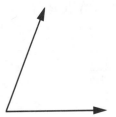

Solve.

11. $\frac{4}{5} - \frac{2}{3}$ **12.** $\frac{8}{9} - \frac{1}{2}$ **13.** $2\frac{4}{5} + \frac{11}{5}$

14. $\frac{12}{5} - 2$ **15.** $\frac{12}{16} - \frac{5}{16}$ **16.** $\frac{34}{20} + \frac{2}{5}$

17. $\frac{3}{9} + \left(-\frac{1}{4}\right)$ **18.** $9{,}000 - \frac{15}{16}$ **19.** $\frac{5}{6} - \left(-\frac{1}{4}\right)$

Practice Set 75

SRB
42–44
180–185

Write all of your answers on a separate sheet of paper.

Find the volume and the surface area for each figure.

Shape	Volume	Surface Area
Prism	$V = B * h$	$S = 2 * ((l * w) + (l * h) + (w * h))$
Cylinder	$V = B * h$	$S = (2 * \pi * r^2) + ((2 * \pi * r) * h)$
Square Pyramid	$V = \frac{1}{3} * (B * h)$	$S = 4 * (\frac{1}{2} * b * h) + s^2$

1.

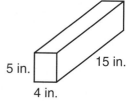

5 in.   4 in.   15 in.

2.

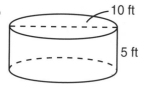

10 ft   5 ft

3.

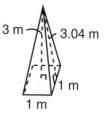

3 m   3.04 m   1 m   1 m

Make a magnitude estimate for the quotient. Is the solution in the *tenths, ones, tens,* or *hundreds?*

4. 8.2 / 12

5. 52.3 / 9

6. 956 / 3

7. 591 / 25

8. 1,226 / 85

9. 12.8 / 9

10. 386 / 19

11. 5.73 / 8

Use with or after Lesson 11.7.

Write all of your answers on a separate sheet of paper.

Ms. Lewis supervises newspaper delivery routes. She made a stem-and-leaf plot to show the number of papers delivered on each paper route.

12. How many paper routes does Ms. Lewis supervise?

13. What is the maximum?

14. What is the minimum?

15. What is the mode?

16. What is the median?

17. What is the mean?

Number of Newspapers Delivered on Paper Routes

Stems (10s)	Leaves (1s)
2	2 5 5 9
3	1 6 6 8
4	0 3 3 3 5
5	2 3 7
6	2

Rewrite the number sentences with parentheses to make them correct.

18. $8 * 10 - 6 = 32$

19. $63 = 5 + 2 * 9$

20. $38 - 32 - 24 = 30$

21. $27 - 28 + 37 = -38$

22. $6 * 4 + 4 * 12 = 576$

23. $517 = 11 * 9 + 38$

24. $9 * 3 + 9 * 6 = 81$

25. $99 = 6 * 24 + 35 - 80$

Write all of your answers on a separate sheet of paper.

List all of the factors for each number. Then find the greatest common factor for each pair of numbers.

1. 12, 20

2. 30, 36

3. 8, 52

4. 18, 60

Write the prime factorization for each number.

5. 15

6. 28

7. 35

8. 40

9. 42

10. 48

---

11. Copy the following table and then write the numbers that complete the exponent table.

Product	Exponential Notation	Standard Notation
▦	10^8	▦
6 * 6 * 6 * 6 * 6	▦	▦
▦	$4^▦$	1,024
▦	$▦^6$	15,625
9 * 9	▦	▦
▦	3^4	▦
▦	$7^▦$	343
▦	$▦^5$	32,768

Write all of your answers on a separate sheet of paper.

Find all of the possible choices in each situation. You may want to make a tree diagram to help you list the choices.

1. Ellen packed her suitcase for the weekend. She packed shorts, pants, and three tops: pink, striped, and blue. How many outfits can she make?

2. A sack lunch from the snack bar has a beverage, a sandwich, and a dessert. The beverages are milk, apple juice, and orange juice. The sandwiches are cheese, tuna fish, and ham. The desserts are apple pie and cookies. How many different sack lunches are available?

The spinner is equally likely to stop in each section. Find the probability that the spinner stops on . . .

3. yellow

4. red

5. white

6. blue

7. Which two colors have the same probability that the spinner will stop on them?

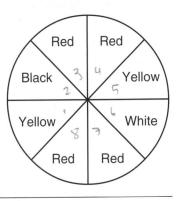

Find the least common multiple for each pair of numbers.

8. 3, 12	**9.** 6, 8	**10.** 9, 10
11. 12, 16	**12.** 8, 12	**13.** 5, 12

Write all of your answers on a separate sheet of paper.

Complete the "What's My Rule?" tables.

14.

Rule		in	out
out = in + 116		165	
		−433	
			97
		114	
			−82

15.

Rule		in	out
out = in * 540		21	
		43	
			4,320
		54	
		109	

Find the perimeter of the figures below.

16.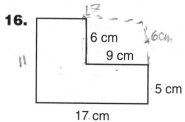

6 cm
9 cm
5 cm
17 cm

17.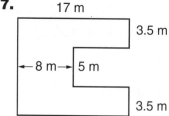

17 m
3.5 m
←8 m→ 5 m
3.5 m

18.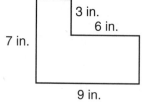

3 in.
6 in.
7 in.
9 in.

19.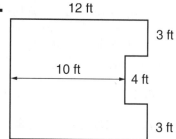

12 ft
3 ft
10 ft
4 ft
3 ft

Practice Set 78

Write all of your answers on a separ[...]

Find the percent of the following.

1. 34% of 500

2. 250% of [...]

3. 10% of 350

4. 80% of 600

5. 1% of 54

6. 10% of 5.77

7. 15% of 20

8. 20% of 540

Solve each number sentence by finding the value of the variable.

9. $A = (2 * 18) / 3$

10. $6.4 / B = 3.2 / 2$

11. $C = (2.8 + 9) / 2$

12. $65 + (13 * 11) = D$

13. $(8.1 + 2.9) / 2 = B$

Mrs. Jewel's class collected the following information about favorite board games in their school. They interviewed 200 students.

Favorite Board Games

14. How many students liked Monopoly best?

15. How many more students liked Clue than Risk?

16. How many students liked Life and Stratego?

17. The school already has Clue and Life for students to play during free time. If it could buy two more games for the students, which games do you think it should choose?

Use with or after Lesson 12.3.

ite all of your answers on a separate sheet of paper.

In a school election, 210 votes were cast. Two-fifths of the students voted for Lisa, and $\frac{1}{5}$ of the students voted for Christy. The rest of the votes were for write-in candidates.

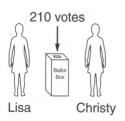

210 votes

Lisa   Christy

1. How many votes did Christy get?

2. How many votes did Lisa get?

3. How many votes were for write-in candidates?

Complete the rate table. Then answer the questions.

Sparkling Cleaners can dry-clean 40 shirts per hour.

shirts	80	■	■	■	■	■
hours	2	4	6	8	10	12

4. How many shirts can Sparkling Cleaners clean in an 8-hour work day?

5. How many shirts can it clean in a 40-hour work week?

6. If the dry cleaners hired 3 shifts of workers so that it could stay open 24 hours a day, how many shirts could it clean in 1 day?

Write each number in scientific notation.

7. 6,000

8. 3 million

9. 50 thousand

10. 70 billion

11. 4 hundred thousand

12. 4 trillion

Write all of your answers on a separate sheet of paper.

Solve.

13. A canister has a radius of 3 inches and a height of 10 inches. What is the volume of the canister?

14. A round rug has a diameter of 30 inches. What is the circumference?

15. A punch bowl holds 3 gallons. How many pint containers of juice will fill the punch bowl?

16. The weight of an object on the moon is $\frac{1}{6}$ the weight of the same object on Earth. If an object weighs $24\frac{1}{2}$ pounds on the moon, how many pounds does it weigh on the Earth?

17. There is a 60% chance of rain for tomorrow. What is the chance that it will not rain?

Solve the pan-balance problems.

18. ($\frac{1}{2}$ cantaloupe)

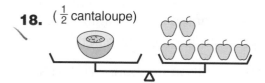

Three cantaloupes weigh as much as ▮ apples.

19.

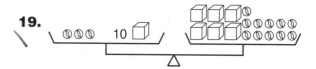

One cube weighs as much as ▮ marbles.

Write all of your answers on a separate sheet of paper.

Write a number model for each problem. Then solve.

1. There are 270 students at Carter Elementary School. Two out of three students buy lunch in the cafeteria. How many students buy lunch?

2. Marilyn had 96 postcards in her collection. One in four are from foreign countries. How many of the postcards are from foreign countries?

Solve.

3. The diameter of the Earth is about 4 times the diameter of the moon. If the Earth's diameter is about 8,000 miles, what is the approximate diameter of the moon?

4. What is the circumference of the Earth?

5. What is the circumference of the moon?

6. About how many times larger is the circumference of the Earth than the circumference of the moon?

7. Mrs. Kennedy presents a program about wild animals using 3 kinds of animals. She has 3 birds, 4 lizards, and 2 squirrels. She uses 1 of each type of animals each time. What are the total number of different ways she can choose the animals for her shows?

8. An ice cream shop offers 3 sizes of ice cream cones and 16 different ice cream flavors. How many different ways are there to order an ice cream cone?